MW00649460

NICOTINE ANONYMOUS (NicA)

THE BOOK

Fifth Edition

Nicotine Anonymous World Services
Dallas, Texas
2015

Copyright © 2015, 2008, 2004, 2003, 1992, 1990
by Nicotine Anonymous®*
6333 Mockingbird Lane, Suite 147-817
Dallas, TX 75214 USA

First Edition 1992
Second Edition 2003
Third Edition 2004
Fourth Edition 2008
Fifth Edition 2015
Sixth Edition 2018

This material may be reproduced ONLY for use within Nicotine
Anonymous, except with written permission from Nicotine
Anonymous World Services

The text portion of this book is printed on recycled paper

Printed in Canada

ISBN: 0-9770115-5-0
EAN: 978-0-9770115-5-1

*The "Nicotine Anonymous" name and logo
are registered trademarks of
Nicotine Anonymous World Services
6333 Mockingbird Lane, Suite 147-817
Dallas, TX 75214 USA

CONTENTS

Foreword

Preamble

Nicotine Anonymous is a fellowship of men and women helping each other to live our lives free of nicotine. We share our experience, strength and hope with each other so that we may be free from this powerful addiction. The only requirement for membership is the desire to stop using nicotine. There are no dues or fees for Nicotine Anonymous membership, we are self-supporting thorough our own contributions. Nicotine Anonymous is not allied with any sect, denomination, political entity, organization, or institution; does not engage in any controversy, neither endorses nor opposes any cause. Our primary purpose is to offer support to those who are trying to gain freedom from nicotine.

(Reprinted for adaptation with permission of the A.A. Grapevine)

In 1988, our fellowship (at that time called Smokers Anonymous) prepared a questionnaire for our members. In 1992, the first edition of this book was published based on responses to this questionnaire. It was our first effort to describe how we recovered from this powerful addiction and how we maintained our abstinence. The second edition corrected many grammatical errors and changed some of the references of smoking to nicotine. The third edition includes the preface, *A New Freedom— Rodger's Story.* The fourth edition includes a revised questionnaire section that combines and reorganizes the responses, an extended explanation of the Twelve Traditions and our newly adopted 7th Step prayer. The fifth edition includes some revisions to the text.

The Four Sections:

Part I—"Our Story" draws from the responses of our members to the questionnaire. It describes our common and individual experiences, before and after attaining abstinence from nicotine, and is written in quasi-biographical form.

Part II—Questionnaire & "Quotable Quotes" contains a summary of individual and "notable" quotes from the responses to the questionnaire.

Part III—"Twelve Steps" describes our program of recovery from nicotine addiction, how we maintain our freedom from this powerful drug and how we live more useful and happy lives.

Part IV—"Twelve Traditions" is a guide to fundamental principles that guide our work in carrying the message of Nicotine Anonymous to the nicotine addict who still suffers.

Preface
A New Freedom
Rodger's Story

Rodger F. is one of the co-founders of Nicotine Anonymous. This is his personal story of recovery from nicotine with historical information on the start of what today is known as Nicotine Anonymous (NicA).

I would look down and realize I had two lit cigarettes burning in the ashtray. The burning tip of a cigarette would fall into my lap as I drove a car. I would have a cold and take cough syrup just so I could calm down my throat enough to smoke a cigarette. If I knew you were a non-smoker, I would take my car instead of yours. I was addicted to nicotine.

I lived to smoke. But I would never admit that to myself or to anyone else. However, 50 to 80 times a day I went through the ritual of patting pockets for my pack, tapping out a cigarette, pulling it out, and gripping it between my lips, finding and striking a match, and, finally, blessedly, dragging on that cigarette. I would feel the raspiness in my throat, the almost immediate sense of relief, that pressure in my lungs. Often I would tilt my head back and exhale as if I were expelling a deep and satisfying breath. Then, depending on how low my nicotine level was, I'd either puff furiously to inject the nicotine into my lungs and eradicate those sensations of physical deprivation, or if I had just had one, I'd leisurely play with it or use it as security stick. I loved to smoke.

I used cigarettes to take the edge off all my emotions, including nervousness, fear, love, stress, and even happiness. Cigarettes were an integral part of my persona. They were part of my self-image. I saw myself as a movie star, talking with a cigarette hanging from the corner of my mouth. I wanted to be a film noir character, excitingly doomed; standing there with a cigarette in my hand and a swirl of smoke surrounding me like the movie poster for Chinatown. I reacted to music with my cigarette. I emphasized my words with a cigarette. I culminated sex with a cigarette. Smoking was simply what I did and who I was.

Phones rang, cars started, non-smoking lights on airplanes went out and I would light up. My friends never forgot that I was a smoker. They knew, they remembered.

How did I ever get to that point where my addiction to nicotine had so consumed my personality and me?

Probably, I was born a nicotine addict. My mother smoked through her pregnancy and I am sure I was first addicted in the womb. Of course, I have no memory of this. I do remember those long trips with my two older sisters in the back seat and myself between my mother and father in the front. No one thought of second hand smoke then, as my mother filled the car with her smoke and kept the windows rolled up to keep out the cold but clean North Dakota air. My father quit smoking in his early thirties and except for one smoking lapse during my childhood; I do not remember him as a smoker.

My mother, however, was a smoker. I remember the cigarette smell on her clothes and hair and all over our home. She was young then and no one questioned her smoking. I think I grew up thinking smoking was a natural thing to do.

When I was 15, we lived next to a family with four boys who were my friends. One named Ralph was the black sheep of the family and it was he who, over the backyard fence, introduced me to cigarettes. It was no big deal. Ralph made it seem rebelliously cool. I think at first I was a little nauseous, but that soon passed, replaced by that sensation of the drag, the long, wonderful drag on a cigarette.

In the small Oregon town where I then lived, there was a cigarette machine outside a gas station that closed at around nine every evening. After the attendants left, I would arrive with my quarter—the cost in the late 1960s—and buy my pack.

I smoked through high school. I demonstrated an addictive personality in other areas as well, using everything from alcohol, to drugs, to girls. I was and am one of those people who, when something has a pleasurable effect on me, must use it to the point of abuse and addiction. Until seven years ago, I had not drunk caffeine for 18 years. Then one morning, I arrived for a job interview. I was tired, having just returned from the East Coast. The receptionist told me it would be a few minutes, and asked if I would like a cup of coffee. It seemed like a good idea at the time, which is also one of the recurrent themes of my life. I had the cup of coffee, I did the interview very well and, even though I was nervous, I got the job. Caffeine worked for me.

A year later after a really busy day of appointments and meetings I went to my doctor around five in the afternoon. He took my blood pressure and frowned. "You've got high blood pressure. I may have to put you on medication."

I replied, "That's impossible. I've always had low blood pressure! I'm a runner! I've never had blood pressure problems."

The doctor was not impressed and told me to return in 30 days to recheck it. I went home expecting to die shortly. I returned 30 days later in the early morning anxious to hear the bad news. The nurse came in, took my blood pressure, and asked me the reason for my visit.

"High blood pressure of course!"

She looked at me curiously and said, "You've got low blood pressure."

The doctor arrived, puzzled, and began asking questions. Finally, he asked, "The previous time you were in, did you drink any caffeine that day?"

I thought, "Yes, probably about five double espressos, three cups of coffee, and maybe a coke, why?"

"And today?"

"Nothing this morning."

"I think we've found the problem."

I am an addict and I smoked addictively. I smoked through high school as much as I could. On my own while in college, I gave free rein to my smoking. I started smoking over one pack a day and then over two. It was the late 1960s and I took amphetamines, studied, and smoked. I drank and smoked. With everything I smoked. I smoked and saved the coupons that were inserted in the packs. I joked that I was going to use them to buy an iron lung. Later, I changed brands. When in Europe, I smoked European brands—at first the ones with filters and then unfiltered. Back in the United States, I found an equivalent non-filtered brand. As a non-filter smoker, I developed the yellow stains on my smoking fingers and picked tobacco out of my teeth. I remember I sniffed my finger at any time and smelled that strong tobacco odor.

In 1977, I began a spiritual journey of recovery in another 12-step program that continues to this day. Unfortunately, my smoking increased, often surpassing four packs a day. The meeting rooms were smoke-filled, and people told me not to worry about my smoking that there were more pressing problems. Thus I smoked incessantly. During a meeting I could finish a pack. If I went to lunch or dinner, I smoked up to the arrival of my salad, and then had a couple quick ones before my entree arrived. I became a life support system for a cigarette.

After I had been in that program for about a year, I was talking to a newcomer who did not smoke. I started telling him that it got better, but was stopped by a spasm of coughing. The newcomer looked at me as if I was crazy, like I was killing myself. I had a moment of clarity and realized that I was crazy; that I was killing myself, and that my recovery was far from complete.

I had had a cough since my teens. I had heard the doctor's warnings for a decade. Still I could not quit. Each year I made a New Year's resolution to quit by the end of the year. Each year I failed.

About that time, I went to marriage counseling with my first wife. At one emotionally threatening point, the counselor asked me a question. I paused, began drawing a cigarette from my pack. Then the counselor put her hand on my arm and asked, "Can you wait with your cigarette until after we've talked about this?"

I replied, "Of course." I hid the rage I was feeling. I wanted that cigarette, I wanted the time it would buy, the relief it would provide, and the nicotine-induced comfort. I responded curtly, and then excused myself to go to the restroom. There I smoked several cigarettes in resentment against the therapist who was sitting in the other room making a dollar a minute. Again, there was a moment of clarity when I realized that nicotine really did something for me emotionally.

I had always heard that smoking was a nasty little habit. With willpower anyone could quit. But if it was just a little habit, why did I seem to always be, minute by minute, obsessed with smoking? I began to realize it was not a little habit but a major addiction.

A good program friend of mine, Al B., called me at work one day. I liked Al because he smoked like me. I never had to hide the extent of my smoking from him because he was as badly addicted as I was. We talked for a while before he told me he had some material on a smoking cessation program and would I like to go to one of their sessions with him. I don't know why but I said yes, and off we went.

At the first session, facilitators described their smoking cessation program and afterwards, prompted by Al, I signed up. After six weeks of classes and a fairly earnest effort, I quit smoking. I graduated. I took up running and became obsessive about that. Then there was food. In the next months, my fiancée and I moved to a distant town in Southern California where I started a new job. We were going through many changes and one day we argued.

My reaction was to drive to a little market and buy a pack of cigarettes. I began to chain smoke. I drove into Los Angeles and met Al for lunch. He was surprised to see me smoking and told me to throw the remaining half pack away, which I did. What occurred to me was that after six months of not smoking, when a certain situation had come up, I had absolutely no defense against the first cigarette. There had been no thought about it. I drove, I bought, I smoked.

However, the next day my mind started working. What it told me is that I had smoked a few, but then had thrown away the rest of the pack and not smoked anymore since. Maybe I could control my smoking. That day I smoked a couple. Four days later, I told myself I could still go six hours without a cigarette. A month later I was smoking a couple packs a day. It was another hard lesson. With the first cigarette, I was a hooked again. It wasn't the first pack; it wasn't after the first week. It was that first cigarette that made me a smoker, when I traded non-smoking for renewed addiction to nicotine.

Years later I remember a conversation with a friend who had quit smoking and become a runner. However, he admitted to me that recently he had started having an occasional cigarette. I said, "Oh, so you've become a smoker again?" He contradicted me saying that I didn't understand that he only had a cigarette once and awhile. He wasn't a smoker. I replied that my belief was that he definitely was a smoker again. It came with the first cigarette. Several months later when he was smoking a pack a day, he agreed with me.

After my slip, I smoked heavily with a maximum amount of guilt. One friend, Dan H., asked me to help him quit smoking. I waved a cigarette at him and told him it hadn't worked. Stephanie S. told me I should start a Smokers Anonymous meeting. I replied that she must not have noticed I was smoking again. Finally, Betsy, an older woman, asked me if the smoking cessation program ever sent me their newsletter. She would like to see it. When it arrived, I took her the literature. She was so happy that she insisted that we both go to the next session. I was too much of a people pleaser and liked Betsy too much to disappoint her. We went. Betsy railroaded me into signing up again.

After six weeks, I quit again. This time it was different. The first time had been easy, a honeymoon. This time it was difficult. It was a nightmare: cravings and obsessions coupled with physical problems. I had narcolepsy, falling asleep uncontrollably, especially behind the wheel of my car. I could barely drive.

Over the years I had learned some lessons in my attempts to quit, especially in my other program. I had no defense against the first cigarette, nicotine was cunning, baffling and powerful, and, most importantly, I had to give it away if I wanted to keep it.

I tracked down Dan and Stephanie and told them they were going to quit. I served up a mixture of the smoking cessation class and a 12-step program. We met in restaurants once a week. Sometimes we had a few people. Sometimes I was the only one who showed up. After a few months I was feeling great. I was feeling liberated from my obsession with cigarettes. I found that God could do for me what I could not do for myself,

I was running. As a smoker, I had always assumed that you ran until your breath was gone. I soon learned that I could run until my muscles said stop and still have plenty of breath. That was a tremendous point of gratitude for me, coming into contact with, and appreciating, a body that I had abused for so many years.

Significantly, I decided to commit to giving it away, to help others quit smoking. After several months, four of us were together on a Sunday afternoon on Venice Beach. Dan, Rob K, and I had quit while Stephanie was trying. We decided to start a meeting and call it Smokers Anonymous. The next week, late June 1982, we met at my apartment in Santa Monica. There were maybe a dozen people. Two weeks later Maurice Z. came and quit. He was to be one of the most important people in the early years of our fellowship. Others came to our discussion meeting where we ate popcorn and drank sparkling water. Soon it was too big for my living room and we moved to a room in Roxbury Park in Beverly Hills.

I was being of service and trusting my Higher Power and it worked. I have not had any nicotine since February 17, 1982.

Those first years were exhilarating. I had a high volume of phone calls every day. We made many mistakes. At first, we decided that one of the Steps did not apply to smoking and we became temporarily the first 11-Step program. Maurice, an author, wrote an article for *Readers Digest* that was published in May of 1985. Thousands of letters poured into the post office box I had borrowed from a friend. In fact, the volume of letters forced him to get a new box. We had no literature so we put together a letter and a meeting format, and some of our phone numbers. For weeks, the members of our Roxbury Park meeting stayed long after the meeting ended, in order to respond to all the letters. We lined up tables and created an assembly line for folding and inserting packages to potential members.

One of the letters we received was from David M. announcing that he was a member of a Smokers Anonymous meeting in San Francisco that had started two years earlier. We also discovered that Georgie S. together with Doug H. had recently started a non-smoking meeting for Alcoholics Anonymous members in the San Fernando Valley. She had recently moved from New York where she had attended meetings there for AA members who were using the Twelve Steps to stop smoking. Shortly thereafter the San Fernando meeting became a Smokers Anonymous meeting.

Within a year, there were a hundred meetings.

The article in the magazine also created controversy. At least two correspondents were from people claiming we had infringed on their legal rights. One claimed that he held the national trademark to Smokers Anonymous and another group claimed to have the California registered business name of Smokers Anonymous World Services. It was David M., who in his calm and spiritual manner, talked to the Smokers Anonymous World Services people and eventually resolved the problem. The conflict with the party that had the trademark continued until the Phoenix conference in 1990.

In 1986, the Northern California members proposed a conference to be held in Bakersfield, California. Thirty-five people from Northern and Southern California came to celebrate our newly formed fellowship. We had workshops. Bill H. from San Francisco questioned whether we were truly a 12-step program; the general consensus was that we were. Through the fellowship of our program, the Twelve Steps, and a belief in a power greater than ourselves, we had overcome an addiction over which we had thought ourselves powerless. The next year, there was a second conference in Monterey at which Maurice Z. became our first main speaker.

In those first years, the San Francisco groups established the first intergroup and started using a small room at the Drydock, a 12-step clubhouse, managed by David M. as their base of operations. Learning from the Northern California experience, the Southern California groups also formed an intergroup with Georgie S. as the first chairperson. Some years later, Georgie moved to San Francisco where she became involved in the program there. She and David became our first Smokers Anonymous romance that led to marriage.

I had become friends with a number of the San Francisco members, especially Bill H., who founded our newsletter, *Seven Minutes.* One day he and I were attending another 12-step program meeting on Guerrero Street. When we were leaving, Bill said that he had been thinking that we should start up a World Services organization. I told Bill that starting a World Service organization sounded much too grandiose. But Bill persisted and with the Northern California Intergroup laid plans to establish a World Services organization at the next conference scheduled for San Francisco in May 1988. This was the first World Services conference. It was during those three days that we established the organization that continues to function to this day. Being elected as the first chairperson of Smokers Anonymous World Services was a tremendous honor for me. Julie W. was elected secretary and Elizabeth D., treasurer.

The next year was an extremely exciting year for all of us. We were putting together an organization that was supporting an ever-growing membership and number of meetings. There were policies and procedures, bylaws, and literature to be written. We had growing pains and arguments where people walked out of meetings in anger. We made mistakes but then tried to make immediate amends and rectify them. People dedicated hours and hours of their time in service to help our fellowship grow and reach more and more addicts.

Personally, I was burning out and had an inflated sense of my own importance. I have heard many people who were founding members of our fellowship describe the same feelings. For a number of years, I was simultaneously the chairperson of World Service and the chairman of the Los Angeles Intergroup. I felt I had to hold all these offices and do all that work because the program needed me. I was surprised when I finally opened up the intergroup chair to elections and was promptly replaced. What I found was that a power greater than all of us directs and guides our fellowship, not myself or any other person. We are all indispensable and completely dispensable at the same time. Just when I think my latest project or job will fail if I'm not there, someone comes forward and takes it to a new level.

In 1990, we held our first conference out of California, in, Arizona. For the year preceding the conference Jack C., a founding member of Smokers Anonymous in Orange County, and I had been working with a trademark attorney to try to resolve the dispute with the person who held the national trademark for Smokers Anonymous. Jack, a former World War II Marine Corps fighter pilot, wasn't about to surrender and neither was I. We came to the conference with various options on how to continue the battle and wrestle the name Smokers Anonymous from the person who held the trademark. Then both of us in the heat of the discussion in Phoenix on this issue came to a realization that we had to quit fighting everyone and everything. For legal reasons and to clearly and exactly define who we were, our group conscience came to the conclusion that we needed to change our name to Nicotine Anonymous. It was a real change in thinking that stirred a lot of emotion. People were attached to our former name. However, we were addicted to the drug nicotine, not just ex-smokers. We were nicotine addicts.

There has also been great sadness for me. My mother who smoked through my infancy, finally quit at the age of 62. I was so happy for her and hoped I had been a positive example. However, some years later the damage done during a lifetime of smoking appeared in the form of emphysema. It progressed slowly. By the time I brought my first baby boy to meet his grandmother, she was using oxygen fairly consistently and would sit by the kitchen table with her tank and mask. My youngest boy only met her once when he was six months old. In October of that year, my mother contracted pneumonia. I flew to her immediately. She lasted three days. The doctor said that with the emphysema, her condition was not very hopeful. I stayed with her almost constantly those days. We talked and I tried to comfort her with her pain. She said, "I really wanted to see your boys grow up," and "Where did all the years go!" She went into a coma. On Tuesday morning, after I slept in her room all night, the nurses told me it wouldn't be long now. I called my sisters, my father, and my mother's minister. They all arrived. We stood in a circle holding hands with each other and my mother. While we said the Lord's Prayer, she passed away. God be with her.

Her death certificate read pneumonia, but without the emphysema, she would have survived. Her mother had lived into her early nineties. I am convinced that without smoking and nicotine, my mother would have lived to see my children grow up.

My sons, Jordan and Matthew, are two of the greatest blessings of my life and they are blessed with a healthy, active and involved father. They rarely if ever are around cigarette smoke and they have never seen their father smoke, which will greatly reduce their own risk of becoming addicted to nicotine.

I love those boys. I love this program.

Over the years we have grown. Many have been disappointed that we haven't grown larger faster. It seems that only a fraction of our members keep coming back and get into service. Many, if not most, use our program to stop smoking and then disappear. It is sometimes discouraging for those of us who are of service. What I know is that, for me, stopping smoking was not the answer. I have an addictive personality. Left to my own devices I will return to my addiction. My experience with coffee tells me that. Even if I think I will never smoke again, why take the chance? I have been given so much physically, emotionally, and spiritually from this program that it only seems natural that I continue to go to meetings and be of service so that I can keep what I have found here.

Today I have respect and regard for my body and a desire to live a healthy life for as long as God allows. I have taken yet another step away from the addictive nature of my personality and toward a compassionate humanity. I have been blessed with a new freedom.

Part I
Our Story

Every day began the same: anxious, tired, lacking energy, groggy, hung over, drugged ... and with an immediate and overwhelming craving for nicotine. The thing that normally got many of us out of bed was the lure of nicotine, except that sometimes we had our first hit even before we found the strength to rise. After the first fix, we felt armed and ready to face the day.

The average age when we began this insane ritual was sixteen. From then until we stopped, nicotine affected literally every minute of our lives. Even as we slept, the drug was moving through our bloodstreams, changing our breathing patterns, altering our heart rates, reshaping our dreams, and getting us ready for the next morning's fix.

Nicotine was part of our every emotion. Irrespective of the feeling or perceived need, nicotine was there. Restlessness, fear, anxiety, anger—there was nicotine. Happy, socializing, cozying up with a book—there was nicotine. Drinking, driving, writing, talking on the phone, watching TV, in between courses and after eating—nicotine was there. Whatever the time of day, the setting, whomever we were with, the drug was with us, was bonded to us, seemed totally appropriate and necessary.

Nicotine was our closest, ever-present companion. Even the colors and shapes of the packaging of whatever delivery system we chose—cigarettes, cigars, pipes, chew, snuff—gave us solace. Advertising could not dupe us, we claimed. Yet brands were chosen according to our sense—manipulated by media and promotional gimmickry—of what made us most sophisticated, most feminine, most masculine, most like whatever celebrity— most like whatever image or fantasy or escape we sought.

Nicotine was our friend, our ally, and our constant companion. Its power kicked us into gear at the start of the day, propped us up throughout the day and enabled us to keep going, and then was present to tuck us in at night. Nicotine was our companion in loftiest gaiety and deepest sorrow. Nicotine was all things, at all times, and always dependable. How could we not love our nicotine?

1

Yet the romance was troubled. While we had disproved what our parents had told us, that smoking would stunt our growth, we were not able to argue with the physical symptoms that gradually began to affect nearly all of us. The scientific evidence gradually built to an irrefutable proof that nicotine was a killer, whether through the agency of heart attack, cancer, respiratory failure, or a host of other horrors. The United States Surgeon General had been putting out warnings for a couple of decades. There was the small print on every package, on every billboard, and in every magazine ad. We saw the warnings, even when we closed our eyes. We knew the warnings. The warnings were deeply ingrained in our brains. But denial and addiction, won the day, the week, the month, and the year.

Getting hooked on nicotine often required a learning process. Our bodies, being smarter than we were, rebelled. We coughed, choked, felt nauseous, and maybe even vomited. Nevertheless, through persistence, the project was mastered. We could be like big folks—parents, movie stars, and other idols. Or we could rebel. Whatever the motivation, we succeeded in learning. We got it right, and we got hooked.

Whether the first encounter with nicotine was alone or with friends, there usually was a fairly rapid transition from experimenting to the point where the drug had won the upper hand. Very quickly, the desired feelings clicked in—whatever they were, whether to be "tough," "cool," "grown up," "in," "out," "rebellious"—and suddenly we were set apart from ordinary folk.

Once we discovered that nicotine could give us what we perceived we needed, it was not long before the drug came to our aid for almost everything and anything. So, we used nicotine whether we were up or down, or whether we wanted to get up or down, or whether we didn't know which way was up or down.

Very quickly, we learned to smoke through it all. Some were able to continue, at least for a while, with sports and more physically demanding activities, but for most, those types of activities—indeed all of our horizons—very quickly became limited.

The encounters with disapproval of our behavior often came quickly, particularly in more recent years. There were implications, or accusations of weakness. To avoid the criticism, a choice often was made to associate only with other nicotine users.

But there really was no hiding from a growing shame and secret fear that a substance was gaining control of our lives and our beings. As attempts were made to quit—proving futile time and time again—a sense of desperation grew, slowly for some and more rapidly for others. There was an increasing thought that we would be addicted until the day we died, and no matter how good our intentions, the drug would run roughshod over them. As the failures and defeats mounted, self-esteem declined accordingly. There was a spiral, and it was definitely downward, taking us with it.

In retrospect, smoking or using nicotine in any form was part of an overall, deceptive existence. It often started with lies to parents—a fairly serious event in the lives of most young people. The lies then were compounded by stealing cigarettes from parents as well. Then there were lies about how many cigarettes we smoked. The lies and deception made the downward spiral spin even faster.

We offer up countless *reasons* why we started smoking. Our friends smoked and we wanted to fit in. Could we be accepted by friends if we didn't smoke or use nicotine as they did? We had parents who smoked, so we knew from childhood that we would grow up to be smokers. Or, "I started smoking at age seventeen so I wouldn't get fat; my mother said it was better to smoke than to be fat." For those who started young, there was the attempt to appear grown up, to look like the adults, especially in the 1940s, 1950s and 1960s, when smoking was an acceptable, fashionable entry into adulthood, a common rite of passage. Smoking was part of the *good life* and every movie star seemed to smoke. Smoking was also related to boredom—there was nothing more constructive to do with life!

Behind these *reasons* hides a grimmer reality: virtually none of us made a fully conscious, informed decision to become a nicotine user. People around us—peers and parents and idols— used nicotine, and we imitated their action, on a dare, out of curiosity, or monkey-see/monkey-do, just to see what it was like.

Whatever it was that we discovered when we began, the discoveries kept us coming back for more. A sense of maturity, rebellion, sophistication, badness, being "in" (with either an "in" group or an "out" group), being "cool." With a cigarette, nothing more was required to become suave, debonair, or rebellious. An instant transformation occurred—from the mundane to the glamorous and beyond. At the least, we could find acceptability, or better yet, admiration and esteem in our own eyes, and in the eyes of those around us.

Our bodies began to crave the physical sensations produced by the drug, just as our emotions began to crave the sense of psychological betterness, which we came to associate with nicotine. Nicotine began to mask or allay some vague, nagging fears—or maybe some more specific fears. Using nicotine masked fear of people. Nicotine masked the fear of communication with others. "It masked my fear of doing something by keeping me seated with a cigarette."

While many of us used nicotine for years without being concerned about it, most of us eventually began to feel guilty about the way we were treating our bodies and/or our pocketbooks. Our awareness of the effects of nicotine increased and we saw that more people were quitting all around us. There was either a heightened sense of feeling "less than" our peers who, seemingly, were able to quit so painlessly, or a concocted idea of being "better" than the quitters—somehow tougher in the ability to continue to smoke despite public opinion.

An increased sense of isolation began to develop out of the same "habit" that originally had "helped us fit into society." This was perhaps not entirely unwelcome, for by now some of us courted isolation and used nicotine to take, or keep, us there.

Nicotine use came to affect every part of our lives: professionally, athletically, in our leisure time, socially and sexually. There was an inability to work without nicotine, arising out of the firm belief that nicotine was our great aid, that it was the fuel that fired creativity. Sitting and smoking usually was the chosen preference over moving about—over doing anything athletic. Sedentary activities, combined with smoke, were the focus of leisure time and social activities. Sex without cigarettes was unthinkable.

The physical consequences of smoking became more pronounced and more undeniable. The loss of breath and voice, or worse yet, cancer and even the loss of vocal cords or lungs. One woman has written: "I believe smoking caused a miscarriage during my 5th month of pregnancy so that we lost the only boy I conceived." Poor circulation and emphysema were also problems. The list goes on. It was part of life to have chest pain and aching lungs, and to know that the poor complexions and facial wrinkles in the mirror were the results of smoking. There was burned clothing, burned furniture, but far worse, was the terrible fear of getting very sick, maybe even dying, because of smoking. And then we smoked to mask that fear, too.

Family life suffered as well. The circumstances vary, but one dramatic story reads like this:

> "Three of my four children are addicted to nicotine and the youngest one I lost custody of. My hopeless emotional condition, fed by nicotine, was a large contributing factor. The child was allergic to smoke and had four fever convulsions before we would even agree not to smoke in the house. The doctor threatened to charge both me and my husband with child abuse unless we stopped smoking around this baby."

Faced with such experiences, most of us tried to quit or at least to control our smoking. The first attempt was usually the latter, with the following among the various techniques tried:

- Buy one pack at a time
- Change brands
- Go places where smoking was not allowed
- Cut down, count cigarettes
- Smoke only at certain times of day
- Quit work
- Pay a fine for each cigarette smoked (but only building a nest egg for the next carton.)

There seemed to be little support for trying to quit, or so the rationalization went. Friends who were still using were probably threatened by our quitting and did not encourage our efforts, though few would actively campaign against a quit-attempt. But mostly it was a tacit support from smoking friends and family, which we managed to twist into a promotion of the continuation of the "habit." (*They don't talk about quitting, so why should I?*) The rationalization also would go something like this: "My entire family (except my mother) found it impossible to live with me when I tried to quit for even a few hours, so they encouraged me not to quit."

The denial that nicotine represented a major problem fueled a continuation of the nicotine addiction. The wide circulation of health literature in the 1970s and 1980s began to help break this denial. The concept of nicotine use as an addiction came later and has been less readily accepted. We thought that smoking, dipping and/or chewing were just nasty habits. Yet our behavior showed the depravity and insanity of the true addicts that we were, willing to go to any lengths to get the next fix. Digging through garbage cans, picking butts out of ashtrays or even the gutter in the street, walking in rough neighborhoods or driving in freezing blizzards in the dead of night, ignoring the great dangers to self and possibly to others. No amount of embarrassment or degradation seemed too much to endure in pursuit of nicotine.

One person related this story:

"It was one of those dreary, rainy nights; a perfect night for staying home. I had just removed my makeup, set my hair in pincurls, donned an old, faded housedress and a pair of heavy wool socks and had finally, curled up on the sofa to read the paper. But I found I couldn't concentrate. All I could think of was that I wanted a cigarette. And I knew that I didn't have any hidden in the house. I tried to put it out of my mind, but I got to the point where I couldn't stand it anymore.

"I didn't even bother to take out my pincurls. I grabbed an old, holey raincoat and put on a funny looking pair of high-heeled rain boots—they were bright orange—over my thick socks. I drove to the convenience store at a shopping center near my house. As luck would have it, I saw someone I knew in the store and, because of the way I was dressed, I was too embarrassed to go in.

"There was a bar a few doors away. It looked nice and dark. I went in there. I didn't immediately see a cigarette machine but there was a man standing at the bar, smoking. I went over to him and offered him a quarter for a couple of cigarettes.

"He gave me three or four cigarettes, but refused to take my money. Before I could even thank him, he looked at me pityingly, put his arms around me and said, 'Are you okay? Can I get you something to eat? Is there anything I can do?'

"I realized that I looked like a derelict, standing there with my hair in pincurls, that old housedress hanging below the torn raincoat, wearing orange boots over my wool socks ... as I begged for cigarettes.

"I assured the man that I was all right, thanked him for the cigarettes and, clutching them, slunk out of the bar into the night, terrified that the man would follow me and see me get into my brand new car. I rode home knowing that I had just hit a low point in my life."

We used nicotine to get over shyness in groups, to distance ourselves from people, and to isolate. Nicotine use put up a smokescreen between us and those we "feared." Many of us felt "sophisticated" while using nicotine—debonair, poised, worldly, powerful, brave, and confident. One person described what nicotine did for his feelings of self like this: "Cool. A quietly charismatic center-of-attention rock star type. Mysterious. Important. I've been there." But another person combines the "cool" and the "positive" with a more negative flip-side: "I felt secure, shameful, poised, perverse, cool, controlled, contrived, but most of all—sick." Low self-esteem definitely was one of our leading trademarks.

Nicotine changed our relationships with others, including non-smokers and anti-smoking advocates. We resented these types. They made us mad. It was possible to get angry just watching public service messages on TV suggesting that we consider not smoking. We felt discriminated against. Public places ceased being safe. One person wrote, "Sometimes I'd be eating at a restaurant counter and someone would complain that my cigarette was bothering them. My reply was often brutally cruel, such as, 'So move down six stools—who needs you?'"

Even the home front could turn into a war zone over nicotine usage. "I had conflicts with my boyfriend. I did quit smoking in bed. He didn't like the smell in the bedroom." Another person wrote, "My father didn't want me to smoke in the car because it got into and stayed in the air conditioning system. Of course, I would try not to, but the obsession to use nicotine would get me into it and then we would fight." Yet another had conflicts with his wife: "My wife lost her first husband to lung cancer so she feels pretty strongly about me smoking. I HAD TO QUIT—period."

Many times, our first attempts to quit were merely because we wanted to satisfy someone else's desire that we not use nicotine. Quitting was almost always with a total disbelief that there could be life after nicotine. We could not imagine the

7

simplest acts, such as making a phone call, without having a cigarette. More complicated endeavors like eating a meal or having sex were inconceivable unless accompanied by nicotine.

We also were blind to the financial costs of using nicotine. Few ever looked closely at the money that we sent up in smoke. "After my first Nicotine Anonymous meeting, I figured it out— $1,100 a year and $23,000 since I started twenty-one years before. A down payment on the house I'd always wanted."

There was only a grudging willingness to admit that nicotine had anything to do with the bronchitis, sinusitis, colds, coughing, asthma, and poor circulation that were our lot. We avoided reading medical reports that had to do with the effects of nicotine. We burned holes in our clothes, carpets, furniture, and burned our friends and ourselves. We caught the burning tips of cigarettes between our fingers, or dropped them in our laps, sometimes while driving. For those who chewed tobacco, we spilled tobacco juice on ourselves and our cars, beds and lovers. We got into accidents because of nicotine use. There was lost time at work and sick days (sometimes with loss of pay). But we were good at rationalizing or overlooking these mishaps, never adding them up to see the big, ugly picture. Nicotine worked its evil in tiny, easily ignored increments.

Despite the fierce and pervasive denial, we tried to quit. We paid for these failed attempts financially and psychologically. "My emotional response to failing to stay stopped was guilt and a sense of impotence. It simply reinforced what I already knew and what I held as a partial attitude toward life anyway—I am crippled/wrong/a failure, and no matter how hard I try, I stay crippled/wrong/a failure."

Reactions to the inability to quit usually included frustration, self-hatred, and a desperate resignation to continue using nicotine forever. Some would become more determined than ever to quit. But before that finally happened, we lapsed back into using for days, weeks, months, even years.

Life as a nicotine addict was based on denial. Most of us felt unhappy and put-upon by everyone and everything. Bad things happened to us and lots of negative stuff fell on our heads, intruded into our lives, and otherwise got in our way. Shame over the addiction fed our feelings of bad luck, causing great bewilderment and animosity. We were plagued with doubt, anxiety and resentment. Happiness was seldom an option.

As part and parcel of being "put-upon," many of us thought we would find happiness if other people, or circumstances, *would just change.* We spent enormous amounts of energy trying to control others, or like Don Quixote, we charged windmills. We procrastinated. We escaped into nicotine and/or other drugs. Whatever our *solution,* we avoided confronting the real culprit— our addiction.

A sense of security in social settings was always readily available behind the protective shield of nicotine. When society and the law began to regulate our behavior by restricting the places where we could smoke, we got defiant and mad, ignoring the rules and breaking the law. The other reaction for many was to tuck our tail between our legs and go elsewhere to indulge our "habit." Whatever the response, it is difficult to imagine how the ever-increasing regulation of smoking could have had any positive effect on our self image.

The people in our lives were concerned for our lives, but rarely to any effect. Family, children, loved ones, friends and colleagues cared about us and were worried about our nicotine addiction. They were concerned; they were annoyed; they complained; they cajoled; they begged. We continued to use.

Almost all of us had adverse physical symptoms of one type or another, running the gamut from just bad breath, stinky fingers, and tight chest, to cancer, emphysema, high blood pressure, and heart problems. We all had something, however much we denied it or attempted to ignore the symptoms.

To facilitate the denial, we designed some system or other to camouflage the smell on ourselves and in our homes, cars, and offices. We cleaned and scrubbed. We used toothpaste, mouthwash, mints, candy, gum, perfume, and cologne. We opened windows, bought smoke-eating machines, used disinfectants, vinegar, ammonia, incense, scented candles. One person baked muffins:

> "When my mother was coming to my house, I would air it out for hours. Then I would bake a batch of blueberry muffins because the scent of the muffins would permeate the house and make it smell wonderful. My mother could never understand why I ate so many blueberry muffins."

But no matter what we did to attempt to erase the nicotine addiction from our lives, we still stank and so did our clothes, our cars, our homes and our offices. We also polluted the physical environment around us by tossing a cigarette or cigar butt, emptying a pipe or spitting tobacco juice on the sidewalk, in the rose garden, on the beach, or wherever. We dumped our car ashtray filled with butts, ashes and matches in a parking lot, and otherwise pretty much left our litter like a filthy trail any and every place we went.

On the psychological level, our inability to escape from the grips of nicotine had a devastating impact on our self-esteem, our self-respect and our self-love. Coming to realize that this was true was a slow process. Taking action upon the realization took even longer. Even though we knew for years that we should quit, we didn't believe it ever could come to pass.

Nonetheless, most of us tried something along the way, and the variety of options was great. We tried the cold turkey—white knuckle approach. We cut back, switched brands, went from non-filter to filter and onward to "lights." We paid a lot of money for commercial programs, or spent a modest sum on health society offerings. We used acupuncture, hypnosis, behavior modification, meditation, and we chewed nicotine gum. But none of it worked. To be sure, some of us managed to stop using nicotine for various periods of time with one or more of these approaches, and in some cases, the period off nicotine stretched over a period of many months, or even years. Ultimately, the drug won out. Back in nicotine's clutches, we set up new denials and rationalizations, and succumbed once more to the addiction.

Despite our best attempts at denial, we were killing ourselves, and we knew it. We were killing not only our bodies, but our spirits as well. "I was psychologically tortured about being a smoker for all of the years that I smoked. I would call it a feeling of dichotomy or schizophrenia." We all know something of the strain of this personal dishonesty. We said we were going to quit soon, yet we knew we were lying.

Our bodies were warning of illness, but the messages got sidetracked as the craving for nicotine overpowered reason. And so we continued. Gradually, there was an increasing sense of being sick and tired of being sick and tired. "I never really associated being sick and tired with smoking. I did know that my morning hack was a direct result of cigarettes and that my shortness of breath in the evenings was because I smoked too much throughout the day. But it didn't click that I was sick from the cigarettes."

Our minds played strange games around nicotine. All these games were designed to perpetuate our denial and our inability to take responsibility for our lives. By refusing to accept responsibility for being addicted to nicotine, we took away the ability to stop. Somehow, we ultimately reached a point of desperation where we could not stand the lies, deceit and self-destruction any longer, and we found our way to Nicotine Anonymous. The initial reaction may have been less than positive. One person describes his first meeting like this: "I thought it was the craziest bunch of goons and religious nuts I'd ever seen congregated in one place. I thought virtually everyone there was whacko and I couldn't understand why I was there or what on earth these jerks could do for me, and I was very disturbed by the God stuff. When I attempted to inquire about it, I was told that I could not ask any questions until after the meeting was over. But I came back anyway. I was just that desperate."

Whether we liked the first meeting or not, there was some sense of hope—or at least resignation that this was the last possibility of hope. There was a core of people, with varying degrees of success, all actively working to live free of nicotine. Success was not instantaneous for all or necessarily "forever." A return to using nicotine was part of the process of getting to the real "bottom" in some instances.

"After three months of Nicotine Anonymous and being free of nicotine, I had a slip and smoked for a month again. That one month was sheer and utter hell, which got worse and worse, disastrously so. One day, I simply couldn't go any lower. I thought I was going to lose my mind, and I think I would have if I had not decided then and there that there could be no more nicotine for me."

Hitting bottom. Getting to where "death looks like a holiday." Getting to that point where we are willing to go to any length not to use nicotine. Finally becoming willing to confront the reality of the problems we were trying to camouflage behind the smokescreen. Being ready for the process to begin. "I realized that I had needed to wait for the miracle to happen in God's time, not mine."

However we got to Nicotine Anonymous and however desperate we may have been at the time, there was the nagging fear and doubt about whether we could quit. After all the failures, all the false starts, all the best intentions, there was little hope. "I hoped against all odds that I could quit and stay quit." The fear of another failure loomed very large. The thought of never using nicotine again had caused failure so many times in the past, and we had trouble imagining that it wouldn't happen again.

"One day at a time" really was a totally new concept for us. It was something different from anything else we'd ever tried. Perhaps without thinking about it, or even being aware of the notion, the concept of "staying quit only for today" lessened the terror of next week, next month, next year, and the rest of life alone without our "friend."

Another new idea was powerlessness. That is the First Step of Nicotine Anonymous—admitting our lack of power over nicotine. The admission requires an acknowledgment that we, as individuals, have failed and that the drug has won. And it requires us to recognize that we will continue to fail. Acceptance of powerlessness requires acknowledging that all of our self-loathing and past failures are destined to continue and repeat themselves until by all odds we end up killing ourselves. Some of us knew we were powerless over nicotine when we first came to Nicotine Anonymous. "I had to recognize my powerlessness because of the total control nicotine had over me." Or, "I could not ignore all the many, many times I had failed to quit, so I must have been powerless over nicotine." Or, "Just the idea of quitting made me shrink like a spider on a hot stove, so I knew that it was bigger than me." For others, awareness of the concept came later—"that day, six or so weeks out, when I could have killed for a cigarette." And yet for others there was sort of a middle ground: "I guess I knew I was powerless, but it didn't acquire any meaning until I got so terribly sick, and yet, was still unable to stop."

However and whenever we came to accept our powerlessness, we then had to confront the concept of a Higher Power—the "power greater than ourselves." For some, particularly those with strong religious beliefs or practices, or with experience in some other 12-step Program, the idea was not difficult, or at least the concept of a Higher Power was not something totally foreign. For others, however, the initial confrontation with the idea of a Higher Power was just that—a confrontation. "Higher Power? You gotta be kidding!" "Don't give me your crazy religious stuff; I'm here to quit smoking." A miracle of the program is that the same skeptic who initially thought that the idea must be a joke now says, "I'm on my knees most mornings praying to my Higher Power." Others of the initial skeptics write of their later thoughts as follows: "Peace of mind and my very sanity depend on being able to surrender to my Higher Power." "My Higher Power is the 'thing' that lets the nicotine craving wash over me and protects me from having to give in to the urge."

For most of us, before we could admit our own powerlessness over nicotine and recognize even the possible role that a Higher Power might play in rescuing us from our drugged-out insanity, we had to "hit bottom." Various terms and descriptive phrases can be substituted as a way of expressing the idea of "hitting bottom." Getting to "Total Desperation City." "Quit Smoking or Die." Being jolted awake by the "raw emotional state I was in." "Getting rattled to the core so as to dare to 'go to any lengths' not to use nicotine." To be so desperate, so far down, so lost, so sick that we can grasp in our brains and in our guts that nothing is more important than not taking that next hit of nicotine. To be able to live the line, "Don't smoke even if your ass falls off!" Hitting Bottom. Definitely not a fun place to be! For some of us, though, we need to reach a real "down place" before we can entertain the notions of getting "up" and into Recovery.

As we come to more meetings, we find that our attitudes gradually change. In spite of feeling certain that we will never be free of nicotine addiction, we are not using the drug. We learn to turn our will and our lives over to a power greater than ourselves. We are learning humility and compassion. We gain more self-confidence and begin to understand for the first time how serious our nicotine addiction really is—how it affects us spiritually as well as physically. We experience courage and hope. We find lessons in faith and tolerance at meetings and in daily living. We feel that we need to maintain honesty, both to ourselves and to others, to successfully remain free of nicotine.

The Serenity Prayer reminds us that we cannot change the urges or cravings for nicotine. In a broader sense, we learn to use the concepts in the prayer as tools for coping with the many things in daily life over which we have no power. At the same time, we learn that what we can change is ourselves, our attitudes, our thinking, the way we act and react. This applies both to our nicotine addiction and to life in general.

A Higher Power guides us to healthy choices if we remain open to being guided. For many, particularly during the first year of recovery, the main concern is with avoiding nicotine. Sooner or later, though, the compulsion does lift, and then our concerns can turn to nurturing an on-going spiritual program.

Our lives have improved since coming to Nicotine Anonymous. We feel better and look better. However, we experience our feelings with more intensity than ever before. At times, this emotional intensity leads to the thought that we are worse off than before. But as we learn to use the tools of recovery in all the challenges we meet in our lives, we find more serenity and hope than we could previously have imagined. Out of that awareness comes the realization of how much better off we are.

We learn that good people can do bad things, and that we need not take ourselves quite so seriously. Through surrender and the acceptance of powerlessness, we find that we need not be slaves to nicotine or the tobacco or the advertising industry anymore. We find that we can do hard things and that our feelings and fears are not unique. We take better care of ourselves as we learn to live one day at a time.

We reach out to others now as we take responsibility for our own peace and happiness. We have learned to believe in miracles. Most of us are not quite ready yet for the "parting of the sea" type miracle, but on a personal level, we believe in miracles because we are seeing one every day in ourselves. We experience a spiritual awakening of our own being which is as individual and personal as each of us. There is a new vitality, a life, a sense of forward or upward movement, and purpose that never had been there before.

We feel safe, one day at a time, that we will not use nicotine. As long as we stay close to our groups and our program, we feel our chances of not using nicotine increase dramatically. Sometimes we find ourselves craving sugar or other sweets, or salty or fatty food, or alcohol or other drugs or sex—something to take us away—and the intensity of the craving may be surprising. Many feel more anger than they did while using nicotine. In reality though, we were just as angry as before. The feeling was deadened by the drug.

We learn how not to react so quickly. We learn to turn to our Higher Power, whether through prayer or some other means of contact, and we begin to accept that we have embarked on an adventure. We are no longer afraid of losing control because of anger.

By going to meetings, and through other involvement with Nicotine Anonymous, we remain nicotine-free because we share ourselves with others. We feel our Higher Power working within us. Contemplating the sea of faces at a meeting reminds us that we don't want to begin to use nicotine again before the next meeting. Newcomers remind us of our own desperation of not so long ago, and of what it was like at our first meetings. We are able to express and receive kindness and love in a friendly and relaxed atmosphere.

We who have had the opportunity to speak at a meeting and to share our stories, experience, strength and hope with others who are struggling with the same problem, have found out astonishing things about ourselves. The safety we feel at meetings enables us to share what we need to share, without fear, without feeling judged.

Through listening to others, personal introspection, the help of a sponsor and one's Higher Power, we begin to understand the Twelve Steps and to move our way through them—one at a time and in order. Often we do not perceive exactly how we are working a particular Step, or why, but we know when we have done it.

Experience has shown very clearly that service in Nicotine Anonymous is an incredibly important tool for remaining free of nicotine. There is a wide variety of options open for doing service: organizing a new meeting or acting as chairperson or other volunteer for an existing meeting, becoming a sponsor, making or taking phone calls, organizing social events, answering mail. The service commitment can shift to fit the person, the mood, and the particular day or period of time.

Although meeting formats vary, we all agree on the need for discussion and sharing at those meetings. Step-study meetings are very helpful, especially if Nicotine Anonymous is one's first, or only 12-step Program.

Whatever the format, there is something about Nicotine Anonymous which keeps us coming back. There is acceptance and understanding from people who share the same problem of nicotine addiction. We experience—some of us for the first time—genuine caring, love and support. Perhaps the biggest surprise is the awakening of hope. We who were utterly convinced we never could stop using nicotine begin to believe in the possibility of that happening as we listen to others share their experience, strength and hope.

However, Nicotine Anonymous does not work by itself. Many of us are in great denial about our addiction to nicotine. We are unable to admit our powerlessness over the drug, or have difficulty with the concept of a Higher Power, let alone surrendering to that other "force." Without serious attention to the Twelve Steps, most of us believe that it is not possible to remain nicotine-free for long. Some have been content to do Step One and then jump to Step Twelve, leaving the in-between Steps to the others, only to find that the drug grabs us again when life gets more stressful or complicated. Perhaps we stop going to meetings and simply forget that we are addicts. We take that first hit of nicotine, forgetting that, "one hit is too many and a thousand will not be enough."

Because we share a common disease and a common recovery from it, a special bond develops among our members. In a setting that is safe and supportive, we learn to trust and to take risks about living. We learn first-hand the truth of the saying that we cannot fully know our own story until we share it with others. The relationships we form in Nicotine Anonymous evolve as we progress in our recovery. We find we no longer are the first one out the door at the end of a meeting. We begin to go for coffee afterward and talk regularly on the phone to our new acquaintances and friends. We share more and more of ourselves and begin to explore the interrelatedness we need to develop as functioning human beings. Our isolation is lifting along with our compulsion to use nicotine.

Recovery from nicotine addiction is not a singular event. It is a process of living life. It begins when we stop using nicotine and admit we are powerless over the drug, and continues for as long as we do not use and remember our lack of power over the drug. But the admission of powerlessness over nicotine does not make the drug any less cunning or baffling. Left on our own, the drug's control over us never slackens. Nicotine addiction, like addictions to alcohol, heroin and other drugs, is a serious and deadly disease that remains with us for life.

It is often surprising how supportive others can be when we begin to look for solutions to nicotine addiction. It is possible to find support even from those who continue to use nicotine. When that is not the case, we learn that others can make their own choices. This can help us remain conscious of our decision not to drug ourselves.

Occasionally, though, being around a smoker can trigger a craving. Nicotine Anonymous keeps us focused on just how devastating the addiction is and how grateful we are to be free of it. The urge will pass, whether we use nicotine or not! Letting the urge pass one more time builds on the growing sense of freedom from the drug, leading to increased joy and serenity. As one of our members sums it up, "I'll simply say that since I have quit using nicotine, I have had more days of being happy, joyous and free than I ever knew could be possible."

Probably, none of us can say that the journey without nicotine is without bumps and jolts, particularly at first. Weight gain is a common complaint. Food seems to take care of some of the oral cravings, and we eat more candy, gum, pretzels, carrots, ice cream, toothpicks, elephants, the kitchen sink and whatever else is not nailed down. One person claims to have eaten "all of Southern California."

Eating more often is accompanied by exercising more. Gradually, a balance returns. And as people tell us we look better, we begin to realize that we do feel better, whether physically, emotionally or spiritually.

A variety of new emotions also may be part of the process of recovery from nicotine addiction. Nearly all of us in Nicotine Anonymous discover that we experience more of our feelings and feel them more deeply than when we drugged ourselves. Attendance at meetings and contact with members of the group are tools for dealing with these new emotions. Another tool is the Serenity Prayer, which one person uses to deal with an emotion such as anger: "The Serenity Prayer is in the back of my mind always, and I find I use it often to get rid of anger. Turning things over. I get mad at my work partner and try to control his behavior. That fails. In the past, I would have lit a cigarette and done battle with him. Now, the Serenity Prayer *(God grant me the serenity to accept the things I cannot change, the courage to change the things I can, and the wisdom to know the difference)* lets me look at the cause of my anger and let go of it."

No matter what our specific religious beliefs may have been, or are, participation in Nicotine Anonymous and concentration on the Twelve Steps have led us to realize that there is a power greater than ourselves. The power can be a God, other people, or a doorknob. Our Higher Power is something or someone to turn difficult things over to. One person uses the number 51 as his Higher Power. The idea came originally from giving the urge to smoke the number "49" and the urge not to smoke the number "51." Then, every time the urge to smoke came, he could turn things over to the "numbers," and "51" won out because it was bigger. Now, a couple of years later, he has expanded "51" into being every positive and powerful energy source or idea in his life.

Having a Higher Power to turn to eases the unmanageable moments of life. As nicotine addicts, we used the drug as a technique for coping. By not using nicotine, we create a need for a substitute, but at the same time make room for more positive energy. As one person expresses it: "I turn things over to my Higher Power because my life is unmanageable. I used to sit and smoke and turn my will and my life over to cigarettes. By not using nicotine, I have made room for, and now trust, my Higher Power instead."

Another view of a Higher Power is a candle flame: "I see my Higher Power as the flame of a candle. I feed this flame with all the things I have no power over—my nicotine cravings, my desire to change other people, my egotistical attachments, and so on. And with each thing I throw into the flame, the fire gets brighter and stronger."

To have a Higher Power, one does not need to be religious or to believe in a particular God, or indeed in any God at all. All that is necessary is a connection with a positive force greater than oneself.

Most of us in Nicotine Anonymous feel good about the program and would do little to change it. We want to make sure that it continues to grow and reach those who still suffer from nicotine addiction. There is a sense that Nicotine Anonymous likely will continue to be a part of our lives. Attendance at meetings helps to ensure continued freedom from nicotine and provides opportunities for giving help to newcomers.

Answers to puzzling problems and solutions for emotional upheaval in daily living also can be found at meetings. "I reaffirm my priorities and commitment to a nicotine-free life every time I attend. I get to share myself and get to share in others' recovery. I always learn something."Meetings provide "friendship, support, continued inspiration, vivid reminders of the grim past" as well as "someplace where I can talk about my crazy feelings related to not smoking" and find "serenity and reinforcement to stay clean."

The intense, all-consuming cravings disappear—more or less, or totally. Sometimes there is a potent thought of a cigarette, "but crave is not the word anymore." With the passage of time, being nicotine-free ceases to be a "daily struggle," but sometimes there may be a low-key, nagging feeling. "It's not a struggle, but sometimes I just miss smoking—like an old friend." The addict in us continues to call sometimes.

In the process of giving up nicotine, there are other habits that seem to get modified as well—even something as mundane as not lingering over a meal. There are reports of less caffeine, less alcohol, less cola, less brooding—along with less nicotine. Fewer times staying up late, fewer trips to bars, less contact with smoking friends, less sitting in a favorite chair watching TV. "Just a whole lot of excess has been curtailed."

There is a vast array of activities that have been substituted—such as working out, walking, exercising, developing friendships, attending school, knitting, "being with feelings and emotions I'd been avoiding all my smoking career."

One of the further byproducts of "taking better care" is a sense of increased energy and of reduced fatigue. That is not to ignore the fact, however, that especially in the beginning, many report being totally exhausted as they go through initial withdrawal. There are improved complexions, improved circulation ("I'd forgotten what it was like to have warm hands and feet"), better sense of taste, smell and vision, and a sense of smelling better—breath, hair, hands, clothes, bodies, cars, apartments, offices.

Emotionally, we are much improved—although we wonder about this at times, mostly because emotions can be felt so much more strongly without the drugging effects of nicotine. There are definitely fewer and less dramatic mood swings, and we are less volatile and erratic. Our tolerance level for others increases, leading to less frustration and anger directed inward.

A heightened sense of well-being also seems to work its way into our lives. There are nearly unanimous reports of an improved sense of confidence both in one's inner self and outer self. At the same time, however, there seems to be an increased "fuzzy headedness." Initially, nearly all express a loss of concentration. Yet, we find that our ability to focus returns, enriched.

Many of us report an improvement in our sex lives as well. We had more interest, more enjoyment, more responsiveness, more daring, and more candor. One person says, "The exertion of the sex act used to put me into coughing and choking spells. It was painful, awkward and embarrassing. Now I can enjoy the physical side of lovemaking, as I no longer have trouble breathing." Another asks, "Why isn't this benefit stressed more in stop-smoking campaigns? But, of course, no one would believe it." Probably not, considering the heavy emphasis on sex and pleasure in the marketing of nicotine

Life seems more fascinating: "I am more interested in life. I'm not 'living in my head' like I used to when I smoked, so I am more aware of happenings around me—sights, sounds, people, etc. I am paying attention to and living in the 'here and now.' I am having adventures."

Relations with those who continue to use nicotine may change. In public places, especially restaurants, we move away from smokers, finding seats in the nonsmoking sections, whereas previously nothing but the smoking area would do. Sometimes we find ourselves spending more time with those recovering from nicotine addiction rather than those still suffering from it. Our attitudes toward those who continue to be addicted, however, do not include evangelism on our parts. If they seem interested, we are glad to mention Nicotine Anonymous and our experience. When confronted by smokers, we experience a mixture of feelings such as sorrow, sadness and pity. There may also be a feeling of gratitude and gladness that it isn't us. However, as addicts we may very well be envious—"Why can they do it and I can't?" At the same time, we thank our stars and note how self-destructive and compulsive they are being. "They must hate what they're doing to themselves." And of course, "There but for the Grace of God go I!"

The increasing public campaign against nicotine seems to provide a mixture of fortification and irritation. Pronouncements such as those of the Surgeon General renew our resolve. At the same time, much of the public ballyhoo against smoking and tobacco is so superficial, and demonstrates such an appalling lack of understanding of the power of the drug and of the phenomenon of nicotine addiction, that we easily can be repulsed and irritated by it.

As part of the research for this portion of our book, we asked the question: "Tell us whatever else you think is important concerning what it is like now in your freedom from nicotine." The following random sampling dramatizes the power of Nicotine Anonymous as a means of rescuing us from one of the most terrible drugs available in the marketplace:

"The best part of quitting is not to have to be thinking, planning, torturing myself with ideas on how or when I should quit. Every day of the last five years, I woke up thinking I should quit before it's too late. But I kept putting it off until I heard about Nicotine Anonymous. I *finally* found success! And *freedom!*"

"I have a sense of freedom that I am no longer controlled by a substance. My actions are no longer restricted by a need to do something that is not fruitful or necessary for anything except satisfaction of unimportant sensory pleasures."

"I am truly a grateful recovering nicotine addict, because I believe nicotine is a mind altering drug. The most important part of my freedom from nicotine is experiencing life without the veil it brought with it."

"I have hope now, where previously there was only despair, and this has changed me profoundly. I am grateful for Nicotine Anonymous and all the gifts it has given me."

"FREEDOM AT LAST"

Part II

The Questionnaire & "Quotable Quotes"

Introduction

The Questionnaire & "Quotable Quotes" is an effort by members to share with other members the experience, strength, and hope of recovering nicotine addicts. It is divided into three sections: What Was It Like, What Happened, and What Is It Like Now. The three sections reflect the general process of our experience; we became nicotine users, there were consequences that led us to change, and we found the help we needed through the recovery program of Nicotine Anonymous, its tools, principles, and the bond between members.

By reading the text, newcomers may find responses that help them connect and identify with members who have come before them. By writing one's own responses, any member could use the questionnaire as part of his or her process to work Step Four. Additionally, there are questions and responses with which a member could gain further insight from any of the Twelve Steps.

For those members who are unable, for any reason, to get to either a face-to-face meeting, an online meeting, or a phone meeting when they need to, the "Quotable Quotes" could serve as a means to connect with other members and know you are not alone in the process of recovery. Groups can also read sections together and/or use it to suggest meeting topics.

By accepting that, on our own, we could not stop, did not stop, or could not remain abstinent from using nicotine, we recognized the value of sharing what we have gained from others. Now, living free of nicotine, we offer The Questionnaire & "Quotable Quotes" as one more piece of literature to help further the recovery of all our members. Certainly you may think of other questions and topics to explore.

As you consider and write your own responses, please know that all members are welcome to share their experience, strength, and hope with other members. Please submit your wisdom and recovery stories to the World Services newsletter, *Seven Minutes,* or to any intergroup newsletter.

"Together We Change."

WHAT WAS IT LIKE?

1. *Why did you start smoking or chewing?*

   "I started, at age 11, to be 'cool' around the other neighborhood kids. I wanted to be accepted."

   "Shyness. Nervousness with people."

   "To be more 'adult,' more 'sophisticated.'"

   "I wanted to be like all those movie/TV stars, smoking and drinking."

   "There were social reasons and to be rebellious, but right from my first cigarette I liked how nicotine made me feel."

   "The rest of my family was into substance abuse of one sort or another. Chewing tobacco was my choice."

2. *Did you have to learn to smoke or chew? Describe briefly.*

   "I remember choking and having to practice. I also remember having to learn the 'correct' way to open the pack after someone made fun of me for opening the whole top of the pack."

   "An older friend taught me how. I practiced inhaling, coughed a lot, but was determined to 'master the art' with some flair."

   "I watched my dad dip for years, so I knew how."

   "Yes, I would just keep the chew in until I felt like I was going to puke. Each day I could keep it in longer."

3. *Did you feel peer pressure to use tobacco? Comment briefly.*

   "Yes, the 'hip' kids who smoked seemed to know how to handle situations, and I wanted to be like them."

   "When I began smoking in 1958 it was 'fashionable, sophisticated, grown-up.' Yes, there was peer pressure. I

24

smoked to be one of them, to belong, to appear grown-up and sophisticated like the others."

"No, I was a loner."

"Yes, several of the guys on the team chewed, I was new and wanted to fit in, also be like the big leaguers."

"No, I just wanted to be different."

4. Did both of your parents use tobacco?

"My mother smoked for many years, and I wanted to be like her."

"I knew my mom sneaked cigarettes, my father smoked cigars. I never saw my mother smoke."

"Dad always had a wad in his cheek, and my mother hated it."

"Both parents smoked so much, sometimes setting off the smoke detector."

"They were both very strict about not smoking. I avoided them a lot."

5. What effect did advertising have on your brand selection and loyalty? Were you influenced by either a brand's packaging design and color, its tar/nicotine content, or its flavoring?

"Advertising had a direct effect on my brand selection. When 'lights' came out I switched to those, when 'low tar' came out I switched to those, when 'ultra lights' came out I switched to those and stayed with them to the end. Although I was an addict I tried to choose the least harmful type of cigarette. Now I learn that was all a scam just to keep me buying."

"Yeah, I bought into the mystique, my brand was part of my identity as a teen. Eventually I changed, only to get a stronger brand."

"Advertising did not seem to affect my selection. I stuck with brand I first smoked as a teen."

25

"I liked everything about my brand of chew tobacco. I liked it because it was rumored to be the strongest you could get. And it was manly."

"I tasted a few flavors until I found the one I liked, just a little sweet."

"I was drawn to those images of 'slim' women who were attractive to the guys and yet independent. That's what I wanted to be."

6.   *Did you smoke or chew more when drinking alcohol?*

"Yes, I probably smoked twice as much."

"As long as I was still drinking, I was still smoking."

7.   *Did you associate using tobacco with certain activities, physical surroundings, times of day, and/or people? Explain.*

"I always associated smoking with 'serious conversation.' I always smoked while drinking, reading, and driving. I smoked in my car, in my bed, in bars, and in restaurants. I smoked all day long. I always had smoking 'buddies' at work and as friends."

"Nicotine always started my day, got me going. Then, after dinner it eased me throughout the night."

"Smoking was a way to get a drug inside my body. Anytime, anyplace was a good reason to smoke."

8.   *Did you experience a "high" feeling when you smoked or chewed?*

"Yes, I used to inhale very deeply in search of a 'buzz,' a dizziness."

"Sure, especially when I hadn't been able to light up for few hours."

"My 'high' was from that first hit after a meal."

"Oh yeah, first dip in the morning- get a little rush going!"

9. *Did you use nicotine when feeling lonely, tired, hungry, mad, hurt, and/or happy?*

"I always smoked more when I was tired and when I was hungry. I smoked faster and 'harder' (inhaled deeper) when I was angry."

"I probably smoked more when I was mad and/or hurt. It helped me stuff anger. I smoked when I was hungry as if it was a way to diet."

"Probably used chew more when bored or wanting to relax."

"Tired, hungry, mad, hurt, lonely, happy and in that order."

"I smoked more when lonely. It was my friend. Tired? Yes, it was the pause that refreshed. Hungry? Yes, it was a distraction. Mad? Yes, get more hyped up, madder. Happy? Yes, smoked to feel good."

"I used it as a stress reducer so I could medicate myself."

"I suppose my actual feeling was conflict. When I worked, I smoked. The nicotine seemed an aid to my creativity, but I also felt guilty about it because I knew it was detrimental to my health."

"Did most of my chewing alone. Most prevalent times were under states of anxiety or boredom."

"Smoking was my response to any emotion."

10. *Did you smoke or chew when you were nervous? If yes, did it help and for how long?*

"I always smoked when I was nervous. It helped, but usually for only 15 minutes or less. Then I just had to have another cigarette. "

"Yes. It was my method of stress management."

"Yes, but sometimes it even made me more nervous."

"With my cigarette as a 'fiddle stick' I could pretend not to be anxious."

"Sure, but then the stuffed feelings would invariably return, and I would be at the same loss over what to do with them."

11. Did using nicotine mask fear of anything?

"My smoking masked my fear of people and being rejected by them. No matter what anyone said, I still had my cigarettes."

"Yes, fear of everything! Fear of trying new things, being with people, being alone, failure, not measuring up, not knowing the answer, etc."

"Nicotine is a mind-altering drug and detached me from my fear."

12. Did you want to create a smokescreen around yourself? If so, why?

"Yes, 'smokescreen' to keep others from seeing the real me, because I thought they would go away if they knew who I really was."

"I never thought of that until after I stopped. But I was really hiding, from everyone else, and from myself."

"Cigarettes kept me company when I needed to withdraw and protect myself from other people."

13. Did smoking or chewing make you feel more secure socially?

"It used to. Then it had the opposite effect, but I still needed it. I needed the drug to feel comfortable, but the act of smoking in front of non-smokers made me uncomfortable."

"Yes, in the beginning, but then increasingly insecure."

"I used smoking as a coping device in some situations when I felt inadequate."

"It was cool at first, then later on I was ashamed around co-workers."

14. Did you feel increasingly isolated when you used tobacco?

"Yes. Isolated and guilty and afraid."

"No, I just hung out with people who smoked."

15. When did you smoke your day's first cigarette or take your first chew?

"Usually as soon as I turned the alarm clock off."

"I got up, went to the toilet, made a cup of coffee and lit up."

"First thing when I got out of bed, or in bed."

"As soon as I had a place to spit."

16. Then how did you feel?

"Relieved."

"I was dragging."

"I couldn't wait for second and third smokes."

"Disgusted with myself, again."

"Like my circulation was beginning to flow; could go on with my day."

17. How long before the next cigarette or dip?

"Right away. I chain smoked."

"As soon as I poured a cup of coffee."

"Maybe an hour, once in the car heading to work."

18. Would you go to any lengths to get tobacco?

"Yes! I have driven in a frenzy for 30 miles for a cigarette. I have picked butts up off the ground at a campsite. I have stolen cigarettes. I have bummed them from strangers."

"If a store was open, no distance was too far, no hour too late."

"Hunting in the bottom of the trash for half-smoked cigarettes so I wouldn't have to go out and buy a pack in the middle of the night while I was still working, and if I found none, I'd get dressed and go get a pack as late as 2:00 a.m. if I had to keep working."

"I traveled 45 minutes by bus to get the 'right' pipe tobacco."

"Yes, and I did. I went out at all hours for tobacco. When visiting strange places, I would spend an entire day (if that's what it took) finding a place that sold my brand of chewing tobacco."

19. Have you ever lied about your tobacco use?

"I have often lied about my smoking. Early on, I denied that I smoked at all, in the middle stages I denied how much I smoked, and in the late stages I would sneak and lie about restarting."

"Not in words, though I didn't smoke in front of certain people or groups leading them to believe I didn't smoke."

"It happened primarily with a girlfriend, and every time I lied to her, I felt like I was the most worthless, horrible person on Earth."

20. Have you ever stolen cigarettes or chewing tobacco?

"I started out by stealing cigarettes from my mother, I stole from anyone I could, and eventually I stole money to buy cigarettes."

"I used to sneak some out of my co-worker's pocketbook when she went to the bathroom."

"I used to rob tins from the store, sneaking it into a baseball mitt I carried."

21. Has your tobacco use stopped you from getting involved in certain activities? Describe.

"My smoking prevented me (even now, not smoking) from hiking, running, and swimming. It used to stop me from laughing (I always coughed), but now I can laugh."

"I figured if I was killing myself with cigarettes, a physical fitness program would be pointless and hypocritical."

"I chose cigarettes over physical fitness. As a kid I loved to run."

"Countless times. I would not join in groups of people going out after a movie because I wanted to go home and sit there and chew tobacco. I would cut short wonderful times with close friends and/or lovers to go home and be by myself to chew."

22. **Did smoking or chewing affect your performance or choices: professionally, during leisure time, sexually? Explain.**

"That'd be a long list, and I would have to add the lost opportunities, the 'might have beens' that I don't even know, if I had never smoked."

"I've never been athletic, but when I tried, the smoking hurt a lot. Smoking was my leisure time activity. I lost many lovers/boyfriends/dates by smoking. And smoking alienated me from many friends."

"It's difficult to concentrate when you need a nicotine fix. This is especially true when those around you are nonsmokers and you are trying to pretend that you are okay."

"Professionally, nicotine was my great aid, I saw it as the fuel that got my creativity flowing. What a crock."

"I remember one job interview in particular. It would have been a very good move for me professionally. But I noticed a 'no smoking' sign and I knew I couldn't work there."

"Nicotine slowed me down sexually. Who wanted to date a guy with a wad in his cheek."

"My doctor said smoking contributed toward my impotence."

"I couldn't see dating a nonsmoker, and figured the feeling would be mutual. It was even awkward when my partner didn't smoke my brand."

23. *Have you ever been told by a doctor or while hospitalized not to smoke and had to sneak around to find a way to have a cigarette?*

"Yes, when I had a heart attack, I had to resort to looking for butts in the ashtrays at entry doors and then scouting up a pack of matches."

"I was told by the doctor when I was pregnant that I should stop smoking, but I just couldn't stop. I had to hide my smoking from my husband."

24. *Did you feel that you were a "serious" tobacco user that, while others could quit, you would use until you died?*

"I always thought I'd quit, but I began to wonder if the day would ever come."

"Yes, after I tried several times to quit and heard about people who had quit I felt there was something wrong with me."

"I was a 'serious' smoker, and felt committed to smoke 'til I died. Sad."

25. *List some words that describe how you saw yourself when you smoked or chewed.*

"Embarrassed, alone, dirty."

"Strong. Independent. Manly. Unique. Creative."

"When I smoked, I saw myself as: cool, casual, indifferent, in control, masculine, professional, adult, together, romantic, busy, valuable. When I relapsed, I saw myself as: weak, worthless, shameful, incompetent, hopeless."

"Suave. Tough. Serious. Profound."

"Macho, cool, smart, sophisticated."

"Compulsive. Guilt-ridden. Powerless. In conflict. Angry at myself. Fearful of the consequences."

"Self-destructive, a failure, weak, stupid."

"Disgusting, weak, unfree of compulsions."

"In control, meditative, as a pipe smoking professor-type."

"Anxious, intense, addicted, individualistic, rebellious, too weak to quit."

26. **Did it bother you to be seen using tobacco or to know that people could smell tobacco on you?**

"I was increasingly embarrassed by my smoking. I didn't realize until after I quit that everyone could smell it on me."

"Not really. I didn't much care what others thought."

"I had to stand outside my own store in the cold, it was so humiliating."

27. **How did you try to overcome the smell of smoke on you and in your home?**

"I used to spray cologne in my hair and used breath spray. I opened windows and sprayed with air fresheners."

"Sprays, open windows, incense, but still stank anyway."

"I didn't bother. The place just reeked of smoke."

"I open windows and lots of washing and scrubbing."

28. **Did you ever think of yourself as "less than others" because you couldn't quit using nicotine?**

"Yes, very much. I think that it was that feeling I most wanted to be rid of and the reason I decided to quit."

"I always thought of myself as 'less than others' because I smoked, period. I could always quit and did 50–60 times, but I always smoked again, and because it was unhealthy, I was 'less than.'"

"When I was young I thought smoking made me 'more than others,' then age and reality started to knock me on the head until I felt like a jerk with a jones."

29. While still using tobacco, could you imagine life and your usual activities without nicotine?

"To make a phone call was unthinkable without first getting cigarettes, lighter, and ashtray stationed by the phone. Then, I'd light up ... and dial."

"No. Life, any routine activity, was inconceivable without nicotine. It was me and my tobacco against the world, to get through the day."

"NO! One reason to eat was simply for that good smoke afterwards."

"Only imagine it in my daydreams, until a craving snapped me out of it."

30. Did you see yourself as a nicotine addict while using tobacco?

"No, I thought it was just a bad habit."

"I knew I was hooked, but it wasn't until I tried nicotine gum that I realized I had a physical addiction to nicotine."

"Even though I was sober two years in another fellowship, when I quit smoking I never connected smoking to being addicted, not in those words, until I came to Nicotine Anonymous."

"I just joked that I was a 'nicotine fiend' as if that was cool thing to be."

31. Were you troubled by the irrationality of your behavior?

"I never saw my behavior as irrational, even though I knew cigarettes were bad for me. I was not 'irrational,' smoking was just something I did."

"I wouldn't have used that word then. I saw it as a bad habit, something I was going to stop 'one of these days.'"

"Mostly I blocked thoughts about it, until I came to Nicotine Anonymous. NicA ruined my smoking."

"Of course I was troubled by the irrationality of my behavior. Smoking kills. I didn't want to kill myself. But I was and am an addict."

"Sure, and I used excuses to 'medicate' the 'dis-ease' I felt."

"Yes. I didn't understand it, or wasn't willing to try to understand."

32. *Did you feel guilty about smoking or chewing?*

"I often felt guilty for smoking after I tried to quit the first time and relapsed. Just about every cigarette after that was guilt-ridden. Before then, I thought smoking was good and wondered why some people complained."

"Yes, especially when my daughter said she was afraid I would die."

"At the end, people would occasionally complain about my smoking. I hated this, but I knew they were right. I wouldn't admit they were right, but inside, I felt guilty."

33. *Did you feel unattractive because you smoked or chewed?*

"Originally, I felt 'cool' because I smoked, but eventually it registered with me that it was very silly looking and unattractive."

"The last few years of my smoking it no longer seemed like a sophisticated thing to do. I didn't want to be 'that kind' of person anymore."

"Felt AND looked unattractive, with the wrinkles around my mouth, and my kids told me how bad I smelled. "

"Only when I chewed around women, but I did it anyway."

34. *Did you ruin clothes, linens, or furniture with burns or ashes?*

"I burned everything: car seats, clothes, furniture, carpets, linens, other people's things, and even other people."

35

"You name it, nothing was safe. One of the worst was a burn mark I left on a neighbor's expensive piano that could not be repaired."

"I would occasionally spill my spit cup contents from chewing tobacco on myself and important things such as term papers, books, carpet, car seats, and even other people. Until you've done it, you don't know how disgusting it is to have to clean it up."

35. *Did you start to feel like a polluter? Did tossing cigarette butts or spitting begin to bother you?*

"I never really felt like a polluter, and tossing cigarette butts never bothered me because they were so small. I see now that not only was I polluting people's air, but that my butts were polluting the landscape and possibly even starting fires."

"Spitting was mindless until I wanted to quit, then it bothered me, so I swallowed more often."

36. *Did the cost of using tobacco worry you? Did you think about how many dollars per year you spent on tobacco?*

"The cost of smoking didn't worry me until my last relapse. Up until then, cigarettes were a higher priority than money."

"Never really thought of the total cost. Vaguely, I knew it was a lot. After my first NicA meeting, I figured it out: $1100 per year and $23,000 since I started. A down payment on the house I'd always wanted."

"Annoyed about the 'luxury tax,' but liked smoking as if a 'luxury.'"

"I didn't think about it beyond each purchase, certainly not for a year/life."

"Never. The addiction always lived in absolute luxury at the expense of all else."

37. Did you have health problems connected with tobacco use?

"Out of breath, cruddy tongue."

"Nicotine affected my peripheral circulation."

"Heart disease, plaque buildup in an artery."

"Emphysema has me carrying around an air tank."

"Needed kidney surgery, but doctor would not perform it until I quit smoking. I struggled with that, and the time it took me to quit had me scared every day. What a nightmare."

"Tooth damage and gum disease my dentist told me was due to tobacco use. Cost me a fortune to treat."

"Two words you never want to hear: Lung cancer."

"I didn't realize it until after I quit, but I must have been allergic because the constant headaches stopped as soon as I stopped smoking."

"Hard to catch my breath, even after mild exertion. Lots of coughing. "

"Wrinkles, raspy voice, yellow fingers next to my nail polish- cute."

"Pains in my chest, poor circulation, pains in my arm, arms and legs falling asleep a lot, headaches, sores in my mouth."

"Hacking up phlegm, even blood. No energy, just nervous energy."

"Sometimes it triggered my asthma attacks. There's an example of insanity."

38. Other than health, what is the worst consequence of your nicotine use?

"I was not fully living for those 20 years. Not discovering my potential until middle-age."

"Living in constant fear. The prospect of lung cancer or heart attack."

"That my kids followed my example. A regret that will never be relieved."

"Psychologically. I felt less than. I felt that I would never really do the things I wanted. Especially in the areas of writing and finding a mate."

"Nicotine killed my spirit. It took away joy and life from my body. It numbed me out. It deadened all sense of adventure and freshness and wonder. It limited my ability to love."

39. *Was it uncomfortable to be around non-smokers?*

"I always pretended that it was no big deal to be around nonsmokers, but it was a total pain in the 'butt.' I had to go outside, interrupt conversations, watch them wave their hands at smoke, cough, move around to get away. This was work for them, but embarrassing for me. Also, when I lived with my sisters for two years (both non-smokers) I had to smoke on the front or back porch regardless of the weather."

"Yes. I felt they were judging me and looking down on me."

"I'd be ready to defend against a comment, but actually, I envied them."

"I just didn't care. I was going to do what I wanted. To each their own."

40. *How did your smoking or chewing affect those around you?*

"My family hated it. My mate complained that it affected our intimacy."

"I think people who knew me and loved me put up with it and accepted it. But a lot of people were very grossed out by it. I must say, there was something I liked about being associated with being gross."

"It upset my children. I know now that my smoking probably caused many of their ear and sinus infections. I can only hope there won't be long term damage, but I could have increased their risk of future diseases."

41. Did you have conflicts with others as a result of your smoking or chewing? If so, describe an incident.

"When I was married, my husband wouldn't let me smoke in the house. Of course I did it anyway when I thought I could get away with it. He would reprimand me like I was a child. One time he said something to the effect 'You'd rather smoke than be with me.' I knew he was right and there was really nothing I could say. I wanted it to be different, but felt I had no control."

"Yes, the smell from pipe smoking was nasty to others."

"My kids were constantly pleading and even angry at me. I didn't know how to explain my behavior. Too often I got angry back at them, even though they were right."

"I had an addict attitude, selfish. I was defensive and aggressive. 'Don't get between me and my needs' was my motto."

42. How did smoking regulations affect you?

"I stayed away from places where I couldn't smoke, even if there was something going on I wanted to see. I could go an hour without a cigarette, so would sometimes brave a short event in hostile territory."

"I remember how pissed off I was when they would no longer let you smoke in movie theaters."

"It bothered me, but did not get me to stop. If anything it helped me entrench against them and I used that as an excuse to smoke even more."

"Generally avoided restricted areas, until restaurants and bars went smoke-free. Then I had to either go outside with the 'huddled masses yearning' or endure the discomfort. That law prodded me into NicA to quit."

43. Were you defiant toward any person, regulation or propaganda that suggested you should quit?

"'Defiant was my middle name. I always had trouble with authority."

"Even though I knew it was illegal, I smoked in nonsmoking areas, flicked lit butts out my car window, dropped crumpled packs on the ground. To me, I was a rebel, to others, probably a jerk."

"It made my wife very anxious and frustrated, especially after my doctor told me I had serious lung problems. And I still didn't stop."

"I smoked more privately. I didn't want people to see me as 'a smoker.'"

"No, I welcomed it. I wanted to quit for a long time. The societal pressure merely reinforced my growing resolve to quit."

"Sometimes I would swallow the tobacco juice, but more often I'd just spit it whenever and wherever."

44. Did the Surgeon General's warning have any effect on you?

"The Surgeon General's warning was completely ignored, simply another ink mark on a package which I did not read."

"Yes, it made me think I should quit *sometime* in the future. With that so-called 'plan' it let me believe I wasn't a complete idiot."

"It did not stop me from smoking for many years. It did, however, add to my guilt."

"Yes, I laughed. I was proud to be 'hard core' smoker. How foolish."

"It always bothered me some, then a lot when he compared nicotine addiction to heroin. It was one factor of my stopping."

45. How did you try to control your tobacco use?

"Counting cigarettes, looking at the clock, deciding when I would smoke and how long the pack would last. Buying them by the pack instead of by the carton, telling myself this pack would be the last."

"Set goals, limits, etc. but it didn't work."

"Eventually, I wouldn't smoke in the house or car or around my kids, which seemed like control. But then, too often, I was choosing to smoke rather than more spend time with my kids. Control? I was out of control."

II. WHAT HAPPENED

46. *What made you realize that "NOW" is the time to stop? Was there a particular situation, person or place related to your doing something about your nicotine addiction?*

"No, it has been gnawing at me for years. I simply couldn't tolerate the guilt any longer."

"Many of my friends have quit smoking. Some of them were as addicted as I. I felt if they could find a way to quit, so could I."

"My 10 year-old daughter watched me coughing guts, and she cried."

"Intubation—being on life support system."

"A lot of things in my life were all pointing to stopping smoking."

"I realized that I'd been saying, when I'm 30 I'll stop, when I get it together I'll stop, when I'm more relaxed I'll stop, when I get organized I'll stop. I was always pushing it into the undefined future. Finally, I accepted that the future was now, life was staring me in the face."

"The guilt became too great for me to cope with. I love my life. I want to live it. An aunt died of emphysema. An uncle is in treatment for lung cancer. Another uncle died of heart attack. Another aunt had a bypass in her neck due to clogged arteries directly related to smoking. They were all smokers. They come from both sides of the family. I'm not getting any younger. I don't want to end up like them."

"I was sick, yet again, and knew that my health could improve in some ways if I stopped smoking."

"I was getting healthy in another Twelve Step program and I wanted to be totally healthy."

"I heard about NicA and took that as a 'sign' the time had come."

47. Describe *"hitting bottom" as you experienced it.*

"Smoking when I didn't want to smoke. Noticing that I had two cigarettes lit at the same time."

"Hospitalizations very frequent before and after quitting."

"Still stuck with emotions and cigarettes weren't working anymore."

"When I was smoking store bargain brand tobacco."

"I didn't have to hit bottom, but saw it coming."

"I ran out of excuses and I knew they were lies anyway."

"I had no doubt that I had to quit and at the same time realized I couldn't do it alone. I remember saying at my first meeting, 'I don't want to use nicotine anymore but I can't stop, I have no control over it. I am terrified that I am going to go home after this meeting and use. I don't know what to do.' It was the first time I said it out loud, and I cried."

"Dentist telling me about the white pre-cancerous sores in my mouth."

48. Did a feeling of dishonesty with yourself affect your decision to stop?

"Got tired of lying to myself and to others that I had quit when I hadn't."

"I knew ultimately I was only kidding myself."

"No. I knew tobacco could kill and I knew that I will be an addict until the day I die."

49. How many times did you try to quit? How long did you last each time?

"Four times over 20 years. One week was the maximum."

"About 300 times. The shortest lasted an hour, the longest, 11 months."

"Quit '1000 times'—sometimes for only hours, then days or even weeks. Quit for good 21 Jan 1984 when intubated for first time (now on oxygen)."

"I tried every waking morning in the last few years. I would wake up and swear to myself, but always, after that first cup of coffee, I'd fail again."

"I didn't *really* try to quit. I just thought I couldn't and didn't want to face the failure. I already felt bad enough because I was smoking. Craziness!"

50. How long did your acute physical withdrawal last?

"Acute physical withdrawal lasted for three to four days for me every time I quit. When I quit this last time using NicA and God, I had absolutely no acute physical withdrawal symptoms at all. A gift from God."

"About a week, and it wasn't all that bad. The anticipation was worse."

"It wasn't a hellish time the first week or two. I think the freedom from guilt was such a reward that I hardly noticed the withdrawal. However, when faced with serious writing deadlines and long hours at the computer, which is where I did most of my smoking, I still, four weeks later, have a miserable time. I do not want to smoke, but I want to run away from my work, because smoking and work were a team."

"A month. Rough, but made me *never* want to go through it again"

"It was erratic. Some days real tough, others easy. For 2-3 weeks."

51. How long has your emotional withdrawal lasted?

"The heavy emotional withdrawal lasted for about 3 weeks and then periodically I get a thought about smoking and 'really want' a cigarette. I have learned to be honest and say 'I want a cigarette' since that is what is going on in my head. I 'say' it today, rather than 'do' it."

"About four difficult months, felt kind of lost until I got a sponsor."

"Feeling deprived and out of control came and went like the weather for months. Now, just have 'memories' that pop up to 'pick up', but as long as I show up at meetings I remember what I have gained."

52. **What other methods or organizations did you use to try to stop smoking/chewing before you came to Nicotine Anonymous?**

"I tried cold turkey, a cessation program, and hypnosis three times."

"A cessation program, hypnotist, doctors, therapists, ministers, books."

"Hypnosis, acupuncture, nicotine gum, patch, a health organization."

"Tried it all, even paid money to sit under a pyramid thing."

"I didn't think I could, so I never tried anything else."

53. **How did you learn of Nicotine Anonymous?**

"A friend who went to Nicotine Anonymous told me about it."

"I saw a flyer on a bulletin board."

"A search on the internet. The Meeting List showed me where to go."

"In the newspaper's self-help section."

"A guy at another fellowship meeting told me about NicA and my first judgment was that this was taking the 12-step program idea too far. Fortunately for me, that was not my final judgment, and I joined NicA."

54. **Did you believe you had to be off nicotine before going to your first Nicotine Anonymous meeting?**

"It never occurred to me that individuals would be expected to quit smoking before attending a meeting."

"Yes. I couldn't go to AA while I was still drinking."

"I assumed so, but was relieved that it wasn't or else I'd never have gone."

"No, because the flyer said, 'All you need to bring is a desire to stop using nicotine,' so I knew I'd be welcomed, and I was."

55. When you first came to Nicotine Anonymous, did you think you could quit?

"When I came to Nicotine Anonymous, I knew I could quit. I had done it many times. My big fear was whether I could stay quit."

"I didn't know what to think or how to quit. I was just desperate."

"Maybe, but I was aware of being led by a Higher Power, step by step."

56. What were your earliest impressions of Nicotine Anonymous?

"I felt I belonged. NicA members and I share a common addiction. They understand my battles, I understand theirs. I fit with them 100%."

"Loved it from the first meeting."

"Silly, but sincere. I almost didn't go to the second meeting- glad I did."

"This is just like my other 12-step program. It might work."

"A caring, comfortable group."

"I have always liked the people. I immediately felt that this was my last chance- if I couldn't quit here, with these folks, I would never quit."

57. Are you a member of another Twelve Step program? If so, do you find that you need a separate participation in Nicotine Anonymous?

"Yes. I consider both programs as all one big part of my recovery. I don't do a Third Step in one program and do it again in another. I had 'made a decision.' I did my Fourth through Seventh Steps in Nicotine Anonymous."

"Yes, but I don't get the support I need for nicotine in my other programs and I think the level of honesty is greater in Nicotine Anonymous."

"No, NicA was my first exposure to a 12-step program."

"Yes, I belong to other fellowships, but I find that separate participation in Nicotine Anonymous is mandatory for me. Otherwise I might 'forget' how not to smoke."

"Yes, separate participation. I go to another fellowship because of relationship patterns. I go to Nicotine Anonymous because of nicotine addiction. There are different issues involved."

58. Did you find that your recovery in another Twelve Step program was contingent on quitting nicotine?

"After months in another program, I realized I could not be restored to full sanity as long as I was still smoking a full pack a day."

"Yes. Whenever I relapsed with alcohol, I relapsed with tobacco. When I finally got sober, I got smober."

"No. I had 12 years in AA before I had enough courage to try NicA."

"I had been going to another 12-Step program for awhile to face my compulsive behavior, which is why I knew NicA would work for me."

"Yes. I had been in another 12-step program for three months and I knew that if I truly wanted to get healthy I would have to quit nicotine too."

59. Have you slipped since coming to Nicotine Anonymous? If so, what did you learn?

"Yes. I learned that I had to ask God for help and use the program for support. It was a good lesson."

"Yes, and it taught me that I have to wait for the miracle to happen in God's time, not mine. My job was to do my Step work, and let go."

"The slip started in my head well before I put that butt in my mouth. Meetings are my medicine, so now I keep showing up."

"Once I quit, I haven't slipped. Service keeps me focused on the Program rather than on nicotine. I believe Our Promises, and it works, if I work it."

"I kept coming to meetings. Members were only people who understood without criticism, so I got 'back on the wagon' right away."

"I stayed away for months, ashamed, but finally realized my pride and nicotine were going to kill me, so I returned and got a warm welcome."

60. When you had stopped using nicotine, did event(s) or feeling(s) provoke you to use tobacco again?

"I just spent $80 at the hypnotist for the second time, when my husband said to me, 'You're so cranky, why don't you just smoke.' So I did."

"When I relapsed, I used any excuse I could find. The last relapse was over sexual problems with my lover. Before that it was my weight gain. Other excuses went from relationship breakups to 'just because I want to.'"

"Upsets, and the false belief that I could control it."

"High stress; situations which would force me to confront deep feelings."

"I figured that since I'd already quit, I could have just one. Wrong!"

"I gave up illegal drugs, then thought—I can use nicotine again, it's legal."

"Emptiness. I could not stand the emptiness inside. I filled this emptiness with nicotine. And when I didn't, the emptiness filled me."

61. What was your emotional reaction when you failed to stay stopped?

"Self hate."

"Every time I relapsed I felt increasing shame, low self-worth, guilt over secondhand smoke damage, but most of all a quiet, desperate, hopeless fear that I was going to die a slow painful death from smoking and no matter what I wanted to do, that was that and I could never quit."

"Frustration, anger, self-loathing, mixed with relief- the constant conflict."

"Guilt. A sense of defeat. Powerlessness over the addiction."

"Deep depression and fear bordering on suicidal."

"Shock, fear."

"Disappointed the first times. Last time I failed, I cried, felt desperate."

"Felt hopeless on my own, but knew there was hope with help."

"I felt that I would literally, physically die."

"I was afraid I couldn't quit or that I would just relapse."

"It was the absolute most frightening thing I have ever faced."

62. *Did you have trouble with the concept of powerlessness? What happened to give it meaning for you?*

"I knew when I came in to Nicotine Anonymous that I was a hopeless nicotine addict. Powerless and unmanageable applied, but it took 23 years of pain and failed attempts before I could seek help from Nicotine Anonymous (even though I knew the Twelve Steps already worked in my life.)"

"I think I was a little cocky when I first came to Nicotine Anonymous. It was after I slipped that I really came face to face with my powerlessness. I asked God for help and I got that help but it was not easy for a while after that."

"I knew I was powerless from the fact that I knew that cigarettes were no good but kept smoking anyway."

49

"I was confused at first because I was looking for *the power* to quit. After months of meetings, trying to control my smoking, I finally accepted that on my own I was not powerful enough to control how nicotine affected me. Then I knew I needed to truly *join* the group."

63. *How long before the Twelve Steps began to make any sense to you?*

"It is only now, as I write this, that I understand how to apply the Steps to nicotine. This questionnaire is showing me my powerlessness and also serving as an inventory."

"It took a couple of weeks and much reading. It's an ongoing process."

"They made sense all along. They were the support system I needed to stay stopped."

"It was all new and confusing for quite awhile, but I just trusted that so many people had found recovery using them- I would keep an open mind."

"I was 'dazed and confused' for months until I got a sponsor who spent time discussing them with me."

64. *Were you surprised to learn that Nicotine Anonymous is a spiritual program and not a smoking cessation program?*

"No. It seemed to make perfect sense to me. I was glad it was a spiritual program and not just a smoking cessation program. Even though it was all new to me, I welcomed the change. My life had not been working. I needed a spiritual program."

"Yes. I wasn't quite sure what to make of it at first."

"The 'God' word surprised/bothered me until members told me it was of my own understanding and no one tried to 'convert' me to a religion."

65. *How did you initially relate to the concept of a "Higher Power?" Has your attitude changed? Describe.*

"I had a child's idea of God which worked for me. But during the last several years I have practiced the Eleventh Step as an important part of my daily life. I have pursued different types of meditation and spiritual paths. It's a very personal relationship with a power that is always available to me simply by going within to commune. It's a continuing wonderful experience and one that I wouldn't want to miss for anything."

"Higher Power, I call God, is my concept of a universal life force in and through everything. The only change was that originally I couldn't say 'God,' and now it doesn't matter and I can say 'God.'"

"I had trouble with the concept of a Higher Power. I do not believe in 'God' as most people do. I believe in some sort of a force. I believe in the higher part of myself. That's the best I can do."

"Through metaphysics."

"I relate to the power of the group as my Higher Power."

"I had a Higher Power from another program who I put in charge right from the start in Nicotine Anonymous."

"I've been a religious person for 42 years, that hasn't changed."

"I've never wanted to be in religious club. Nature has always been my inspiration and spiritual guide. The care of the group and Nature's beauty is how I have my transcendent experience to lift me from my addiction."

"I have always thought of it as God. I have not had God or any spiritual power in my life for years. My coming to the point where I could say 'I can't do it alone anymore' was the beginning of God returning in my life."

"I understand my Higher Power as a Higher Purpose that calls me to act beyond self-seeking motives listed in the Third Step Prayer. Service is a way of fulfilling this Purpose and connects me to that Power and its Peace."

66. ***Do you have a sponsor? Are you someone's sponsor?***

"Not yet, but I have my Nic A members and we support each other."

"I use people in program as my sponsor."

"Yes, I got a sponsor after my second meeting."

"It took me a while to find courage to ask someone, but my sponsor was very helpful. Now I return the gift by sponsoring a newcomer."

67. ***What kept you coming back to Nicotine Anonymous?***

"I kept coming back to Nicotine Anonymous because I knew I was a completely helpless addict and I had faith that if Twelve Step programs help many people with addictions, then Nicotine Anonymous could help me."

"The emotional support that we were all doing it together. The possibility of being free kept me coming back. I never doubted that it would work."

"I belong. The others there share my addiction. I feel the support is invaluable and working the Twelve Steps is the only solution for me."

"Seeing others make it. Nothing else had worked for me."

"The people! Desperation, commitment to group."

"Support and non-judgment about slips. The 'gentle program' I needed."

III. WHAT ARE YOU LIKE NOW?

68. *Do you still experience cravings for nicotine?*

"Rarely. But I still have dreams in which I want and even have a cigarette. I wake up very disturbed, so I know I don't really want to go back."

"No, not cravings, but occasionally if I'm under a particularly stressful situation and I see someone light up, I think, wow it would be nice to be able to escape for a moment. Then I say, thank you God I don't have to."

"I am not feeling the craving for nicotine as much as I'm feeling deprived of my 'companion.'"

"Yes, but seldom. They surprise me, but usually linked to a wish to escape or feeling overwhelmed."

"Not since the first weeks of withdrawal. I've had a 'desire' arise on occasion. But I now understand that I have 'memories' due to all the brainwashing I did. I can't erase them, but I don't have to 'obey' them."

"I don't crave it, but I feel insecure when I am working because I have no cigarettes. Yet I don't crave nicotine to remedy the problem."

"I've totally lost the obsession to suck toxic gases into my body."

"At first I had many cravings throughout the day, but then less and less. Now I have occasional 'thoughts' to smoke, but I don't crave nicotine. Sometimes I miss the sensation, but I remind myself that I don't miss all the horror that goes with it, so focus on all I've gained."

69. *Do you notice an increase in putting something in your mouth?*

"I ate lots of peanuts and chocolate, but I switched to sugarless gum."

"Yes, I rediscovered food in a big way, and I have had to deal with that. It is a challenge. I also go through a lot of toothpicks."

"Oh yeah, and to bite down on something. A member told me about licorice root. I gnaw on sticks and it helps ease that whole oral thing."

"Yes, but I completely accept that a cigarette is not an option."

70.   *How do meetings help you remain nicotine-free?*

"Meetings are a weekly reminder that I am like other members, powerless over nicotine, and can relapse without consistent vigilance and maintenance. I also get to meet and help newcomers."

"By listening to newcomers complain about how bad they feel, it reminds me of what it was like. It also gives me a chance to share my experience, strength and hope as well as what's going on in my life today."

"The support is of utmost importance, knowing you're not alone in this battle, being encouraged by those who have gone before you, getting 'tips' on things that help you through, and being able to share the agony and the joy with others who understand."

"Peer pressure/group support. Reminders of how hard it used to be."

"Knowing they're ongoing, keeps me going on."

"When I speak, I get reinforcement, which is very supporting to my goal."

"Meetings get me out talking and being with people who share some of my problems. They give me the chance to express kindness and love. They give me the chance to receive kindness and love from others."

"The effort to go to meetings exercises and strengthens my commitment. If I get lazy, I could relapse. Each meeting is like a refresher course."

71.   *What have you learned at meetings about living?*

"I learned that the urge for nicotine would pass whether or not I smoked a cigarette. The best news I'd ever heard!

From this, I've learned the meaning of 'this too shall pass' in a personal way that I didn't have before."

"I can live without nicotine, one day at a time. Talking about the craving or obsession and being honest about having the craving/obsession takes the power out of it and I don't have to pick up."

"That I can live happily being nicotine-free, even gratefully ecstatic."

"Powerful things can be done with the help of a group of people who believe in what they are doing."

"Being more accepting, reaching out, opening up more."

"I've learned about taking responsibility for my own peace and happiness."

"I once believed stopping was impossible. Now I know that was fear, not fact. Changing any behavior may be challenging, but is no longer to be dismissed as 'impossible.' Asking for help and spiritual guidance."

"I'm more normal than I ever thought. That has given me both acceptance and courage."

72. **What new emotions have cropped up? What Nicotine Anonymous tool or message do you use to deal with these new feelings?**

"There's so much anger that I didn't know was there before. The main ways I deal with this anger are sharing in meetings and learning new skills from my sponsor to handle it appropriately."

"I had a lot of anger in the beginning as well as feelings of loneliness, grief, fear. I use the telephone to talk with other people in the program. Sometimes I call newcomers and that makes me get grateful real quick! Also, I remember that feelings pass and that I do what I'm supposed to do today no matter what I'm feeling. Sometimes I just say, 'Well, I'm depressed today but that's okay. It's not a big deal.' Whereas in the past if I was depressed I would nurture the depression and really get into it. I don't do that anymore."

"Reciting the phrase 'This too shall pass' helps me manage my anxiety."

"My sanity has been saved countless times by saying the Serenity Prayer. My feelings are more manageable with the wisdom of this perspective."

"I use our Slogans, 'Choose Faith Over Fear' and 'Dealing With the Feeling' because my relapses have shown me I have to 'Watch My Steps. '"

"If I get to grieving my old friend nicotine, I call someone on the phone list and we talk about it."

"When I feel overwhelmed, I take a moment and remember to be 'Grateful for Grace' and I am calmed and remember to take things one at a time."

"I pray, talk to people, practice 'Easy Does It.' It's working for me."

73. *Do any of these feelings endanger your continued abstinence? Which?*

"I don't think I ever feel in danger of actually smoking. But my most destructive feelings are fear of inadequacy and financial ruin. The "F" word: Future. This is the stuff I have to be careful with. I am really vigilant about my program when these things come up, but I don't ever think that smoking would make it better."

"They all do."

"No, I learn to stay with the feelings and deal with them."

"No, none of the stuff I'm going through makes me want to use nicotine. Nicotine represents poison and death. I'm learning a new method of coping with my anxieties and angers."

"Feeling less acceptable with my gained weight."

74. *Do you feel more anger than you did while using nicotine? If so, how do you deal with it?*

"At first I felt more anger because I'd been stuffing it for so long. Now I feel that I'm less angry and I use the Steps to determine if I'm at fault or if the anger is fair. If it is, I try to express it constructively to the person I'm angry at. Sometimes that's not possible, so I'll vent it with a friend so I can get rid of it."

"Yes. I'm having trouble dealing with the anger. I find myself turning a lot of things over and letting go of things I can't really control. I find myself even letting go of things I can control when they're not high on the priority list or when the effort involved isn't worth the end result."

"I take five deep breaths and/or say the Serenity Prayer."

"I feel more of everything now, but I pet my cat or walk in my garden."

"I pray if I think I might lose control. I talk to myself because I know that if I lose control I'm the one who will suffer more than anyone else. I've learned that I don't enjoy my anger like I used to."

"I use my sponsor or my group's phone list to talk and sort things out. Just being heard helps calm me down and even helps me to look at any part I may have had in the situation."

75. *What attitudes have changed in you as a result of coming to Nicotine Anonymous?*

"I see myself and others more clearly. I'm not hiding the truth from myself. I've discovered I'm capable and have more self-esteem and confidence in my abilities. I do things I enjoy and feel good about it. I like myself more because there's more to like. I'm really living now. I feel positive about the future and my ability to create a better life for myself."

"I used to stuff my anger with nicotine and then get nasty and revengeful. Now I've learned to express that anger appropriately and my whole attitude has become much mellower."

"A feeling that I'm doing something positive for myself. Lack of guilt."

"Oh, I'm so smart now; my IQ has increased at least 20%."

"Being more tolerant of myself and others."

"I have changed my entire internal life. More than anything, I am aware of my sickness when it sets in. My sickness includes feeling sorry for myself, being selfish, dishonest, being the victim, feeling angry and resentful or arrogant, being ashamed, being afraid, and judging others. Now I know when I am doing these things. I also know why I do them. And I make steps every day to change all these character defects and replace them with love, humility, spirituality, patience, fellowship, service, acceptance, courage, and honesty."

76. Do you feel more honest? How does your commitment to honesty relate to your continued freedom from nicotine?

"Instead of smoking 'at' somebody I'm able to speak up and state my truth. I'm not depressed like I used to be."

"I inform people what is on my mind. Now, there's very little 'bull-loney' left in my life. I'm more comfortable being in the world now."

"Yes. I don't want to be full of lies, or go back to being stupid, or go back to the slow death. Honesty helps me see my way forward more clearly."

"I had to get honest to get free. If I don't stay honest, I won't stay free."

77. Do you feel safe that you won't use nicotine again?

"Yes, I feel safe. I know that as long as I am honest with myself I won't start again."

"Absolutely not. I know that if I don't use NicA's tools to maintain my smobriety I will surely relapse. I've done it too often (relapse)."

"I feel that nicotine is not an option for my anymore. But I need the meetings and the support."

"Fairly safe. Always a question."

"I'm scared that it's still a possibility."

78. Is your main concern still with avoiding nicotine?

"Actually, the addiction was to nicotine, but my obsession was smoking."

"Yes. My second concern is getting my work done without using nicotine. My third concern is dealing with my anger."

"It concerns me, but mostly learning how to live my life on life's terms."

"Certainly nicotine is ever a concern, but my focus is on recovery. I've come to believe in the guidance: 'focus on the solution, not the problem.'"

79. Do you move away from smokers in public places or avoid certain places where people smoke?

"Most of the time, but sometimes I'm attracted to move closer."

"At first I thought I wouldn't mind, now I can't stand it."

Yes, I hate it in the Laundromat. I don't want to take the smell home."

"I neither want to breathe those toxins, nor chance triggering a desire. I accept that nicotine addiction is cunning and I avoid taking risks."

"I learned early on to take care and 'avoid certain people, places, and things' and that has served me well. I have better challenges to face."

80. Do you live or work closely with someone who uses tobacco? If so, how does this affect you?

"I do, it has me struggling between acceptance and taking care of myself."

"I work with several people who smoke; one of them is my boss. I have no problem with them smoking. They don't do it in the office or around me. I get the feeling they are a little uncomfortable with me or themselves because I go to Nicotine Anonymous and got off nicotine."

"Yes, and I have to say the Serenity Prayer, often. It's made it very clear how my smoking affected other people and the importance of Step Nine."

81. What do you feel when you see a person smoking or chewing?

"I think of my own addiction. I empathize with his or her need for the substance. I am utterly grateful that I no longer us nicotine."

"There but for grace of my Higher Power, go I."

"Disgust. I feel sorry for them."

" Sad for their suffering."

"I feel joy that I'm not doing nicotine."

82. Do people who smoke or chew react negatively to your having stopped? If so, how do you handle them?

"No. They usually go to great lengths to tell me about how they are going to stop as soon as they get their act together in some way. Or they talk about how little they smoke. But I just listen and don't judge because I had my 'reasons to delay,' my excuses."

"Yes. They become afraid and perhaps a bit resentful. I just let them be who they are. I don't talk up the program to them because I know they are not in a place to hear what I have to say. But if they ask, I tell."

"No, they know it's killing them. I let them see the sparkle in my eye. I let them ask themselves if they can have what I have."

"I understand that this is their 'brain on nicotine'- it's not really who they are."

83. ***Do you feel fortified by the recent public reactions against smoking? Irritated by them?***

"I'm grateful that I quit when I did."

"I am 100% in favor of anything that will help people stop smoking. There is no other legal substance in existence as dangerous as cigarettes. Only some drinkers become alcoholics. Many people drink moderately all their lives. But all habitual smokers are addicts. It is a deadly substance subsidized and supported because of the money involved."

"I'm pleased that an awareness is growing."

84. ***Do you know of others who have been inspired by you to quit?***

"I've been inspirational help to some and that helps me too."

"Yes, I have friends and family who have followed me into recovery."

85. ***What positive actions have you substituted for using tobacco?***

"Some simple things, I take deep breaths, drink herbal tea, chew on a plastic straw or toothpick, anything that helps me relieve stress."

"I take regular breaks and re-read *Tips For Gaining Freedom From Nicotine* or one of the other pamphlets."

"Between meetings, I call a couple of my group's members and we just check in with one another, helps keep my mind from wandering"

"I meditate and pray more often, and maintain a daily gratitude list."

"Either walking or biking, concerned about gaining weight."

"Yes, I am writing and singing again. My head is clearer and I can now hold long notes like I could when I was younger."

"I keep busy working the Steps and practicing the Program's principles."

86. Do you feel that you have more time now? What new interests have you cultivated?

"When my sponsor told me I would have more time, I didn't believe her. Amazing, it's true!

"I went back to college and finished my degree and started a new career."

"Yes, I definitely have more time and I feel capable of new challenges."

"Making toys for abused/neglected/AIDS children and giving back to society."

"Now that I have energy, I exercise. I get my housework done in half the time without all those cigarette breaks."

"No, but more money. I read more, go to lots of meetings and do service."

"I'm more organized now, and enjoy flower gardens I created in my yard."

"I have developed an interest in art, drawing, painting, writing, sculpture."

"Yes, I began in earnest an active spiritual search. I also decided to learn how to play tennis which I had always wanted to do but had never tried."

"Not new really, I am just getting further into the things I like to do, yoga, playing music, exercising, playing sports, writing, being with people."

87. How has your physical health changed?

"My chronic headaches are gone."

"Better breathing, sense of smell, increased physical endurance, exercise more enjoyable."

"As *Our Promises* state, 'Health is a new experience,' and I am grateful."

"My emphysema is arrested."

"I haven't had bronchitis since I stopped smoking ten months ago."

"If I get to feeling much better it will be too much to bear."

"Circulation has improved. Don't have sores in my mouth. Feel better all the way around."

"My general health is better. I have more strength, no cigarette hangovers, I can breathe better. I can laugh hard without coughing. This is a big sign of improvement."

"Voice better, less raspy. No coughing for the first ten minutes every day."

"Can smell and taste again, colds are shorter, more energy."

88. Do you think that your physical appearance has improved? If so, does this play an important role in keeping you off nicotine?

"Yes, because I smile more. I don't reek of tobacco, the yellow fingers are gone, and friends tell me there's a new glow about me."

"Yes. It is positive reinforcement. My skin is smoother and clearer. All my senses are heightened and more alive."

"I feel taller, but maybe it's just that I finally stood up for myself."

89. Have you gained weight?

"Yes, I gained about 30 lbs, but I have since taken it off and regained about 10."

"I gained 35 pounds in the first year. The weight leveled off and I kept five pounds. I look terrific now. People always tell me how healthy I look."

"Not really, I've gotten into an exercise routine and it isn't a problem"

90. ***Did you meditate on a regular basis before coming to Nicotine Anonymous? Do you now? If your practices have changed, describe.***

"No I didn't. I guess sometimes smoking seemed like a meditation, but it was more an unconscious disconnect rather than conscious contact."

"I meditate, in that I sit still and 'listen' but it's not a particular discipline."

"Yes, now every day. It gives me a peace from which I have insights."

"I've started to, but not regularly. I'm not used to sitting still."

91. ***What is your understanding of each part of the Serenity Prayer?***

"The pamphlet *The Serenity Prayer for Nicotine Users* is very clear and describes my feelings and understanding of the Serenity Prayer much better than I could here."

"I cannot change other people. I can't change 'the system,' the world, not even my own child. I can change my attitude and my actions. It's pretty easy to see the difference, but it's not always easy to accept."

"I cannot change my craving for nicotine. I cannot will myself to stop. I cannot change the fact that I'm an addict. I accept the fact that I have cravings for nicotine. The thing I can change is how I deal with those cravings. They don't have to be fed. The courage to not feed them comes from my Higher Power, the group support, and working the plan daily, moment by moment."

"I cannot change people, places and things. I can change my reactions to those things. My intuition tells me which things I can and cannot change. I've been doing this a long time."

"I cannot change the weather, the time I get to ride on the planet, human nature. I can change my behavior. The courage comes from within and I believe it has always been there."

"The Serenity Prayer is my anchor to sanity. Much of my life's stress has been caused by trying to change the unchangeable while avoiding what I could change. The wisdom may be from my Higher Power, or my Honest Perception. Once that's made clear, I am more at ease."

92. *Are you glad for your powerlessness over nicotine and for what it has brought into your life?*

"No, it's a pain in the ass. Powerlessness is a painful, scary, hopeless, desperate feeling and I hate it. Nicotine Anonymous has helped me with it and I am grateful Nicotine Anonymous was there to help."

"I'm not glad to be powerless over nicotine, but am grateful for bringing the people and benefits from Nicotine Anonymous into my life."

"Absolutely. My nicotine addiction gave me something concrete to work with. Even though I had been in another 12-step program for three months before joining Nicotine Anonymous, things came together like a whirlwind once I quit nicotine, especially with my Higher Power."

"I'm glad to understand that I was powerless over the fact that nicotine is addictive and once it's in my body I am an addict. I'm glad I learned to surrender rather than to keep up my former losing battle. Accepting the things I cannot change has brought more peace into my life."

93. *How do you work the Steps?*

"I thank God every day that I don't have to use nicotine today. I pray and meditate daily. I take personal inventory and ask God's help in doing better. I carry the message of Nicotine Anonymous whenever and wherever I have the opportunity."

"In writing. Ink helps me walk the talk. The process holds me more accountable and helps me be thorough. It also enables me to periodically review and revise as I live and learn over time."

"Pray, show up at meetings, listen to my sponsor, and listen to myself."

"Some members of the group and I started a Step Study group following the regular meeting. That helped me focus and learn from the others."

"Three words: Practice, practice, practice."

94. ***Have you offered service at either a meeting, intergroup, or World Services level? If so, how have you gained from the experience?***

"Yes. I started by taking the key to open up the meeting doors, eventually took turns at chairing the meeting."

"I haven't yet. I'm not sure if I'm too nervous or just unwilling."

"Surprising myself, I volunteered to be intergroup secretary. I learned a lot and developed new skills and confidence."

"I served as an email servant for World Services which connected me with people in many other countries. I liked knowing I was helping people get Starter Kits or providing info for a meeting near them."

95. ***Are you involved with helping the newcomers?***

"Yes, since I learned in my other fellowship that the newcomers are the lifeblood of the organization."

"Right now I'm concerned with helping myself."

"As is said, 'newcomers keep it green.' And as long as newcomers keep coming I will have a meeting, and we will keep our Fellowship. I believe in the wisdom of carrying the message and serving."

"Helping newcomers, I learn insights about myself I missed when doing my own Fourth Step work. Newcomers can be a new mirror."

"Always. I give them my phone number and share my experience, strength and hope. Occasionally, they will work the Steps with me."

"Yes, we talk and lend each other support."

"Yes, by being supportive and showing faith that they will do it."

96. Have you had a spiritual awakening?

"I am in the process of having a spiritual awakening. As I work the Twelve Steps, it becomes clearer and clearer."

"I have always been spiritual in my own fashion. It is a lifelong journey."

"I've become more open-minded to possibilities, more able to ask for assistance, more willing to practice the Third Step Prayer."

"The spirit of this Fellowship has opened my heart and re-awakened my life."

"Yes, because the process has been respected as one of my own understanding, which meant I had no need to resist anyone else's idolatry."

97. Have your concepts of "God," however you define the term, changed since you came to Nicotine Anonymous?

"This is a big problem for me. I have major resentments toward organized religion. I do not believe in a 'God' as churches have defined this power. I believe there is a life force and that's the best I can do right now."

"Before Nicotine Anonymous, I didn't have a God. Now I do. The concept doesn't matter. I don't worry about the concept, that will come."

"I've come to prefer the Program's term 'a Power greater than ourselves' because it focuses more on the principle rather than on a personality."

"When I was a newcomer I would not have stayed without the acceptance of each member able to have his or her own understanding of a Higher Power. This principle has helped me be more open to spirituality."

"Yes, the God of my understanding today is different than the concept from when I first came in the rooms. It has been empowering to explore and develop my own faith."

"My concept of God has not changed, but my level of spirituality and its application to daily life has skyrocketed."

98. How, if at all, do you get the concept of God to relate to you and your daily living?

"Through daily prayer and affirmations to myself that this life is a journey and God is the guide."

"I believe my thoughts and my words are creative. I am co-creator with God and my life is actually an expression of God. I don't have to try to 'get,' but only to accept in my mind what God has already given."

"I think of this force as a great spiritual space, something like a vast river, and as I turn things over they go into this space and the force carries them away. There is a higher spirit within myself, which I suppose I rely on more so than the great force. (As you can see, I'm struggling with this.)"

"I put my hand in God's and God takes care of everything (if I don't get in the way)."

"Looking to my God as my protector and guide."

"I get down on my knees and pray in the morning and at night."

"My 'concept of God' is a calling to a Higher Purpose. When I transcend above my self-seeking motives, I serve this Purpose, and I am served as a result. This aspiration inspires my daily efforts, imperfect as they are."

99. Have you become a proselytizer about not smoking/ chewing? About Nicotine Anonymous?

"I would not say I am, however I believe that some people think I am."

"Maybe just a bit. I try not to because it turns people off. I'm less so as time passes."

"It's not my job to make others feel guilty about their smoking. But my friends know I'm in Nicotine Anonymous and they're amazed that an addict, such as I, was able to stop smoking, and they know they can come with me any time they want."

"I keep a very low profile style."

"I can get caught up, so I've got to catch myself. I'm still learning how to carry the message appropriately. I want to help, not hinder."

100. What factors do you think keep people coming back to meetings?

"In the beginning, identification with others and hope. Then, the caring bond for one another and for the meeting itself, the feeling of having a home group. They also fulfill a desire to carry the message."

"The success stories, but more than anything, having a place where I could share my problems was the major draw. Chips were the tool that got me into Nicotine Anonymous and I love them."

"The desire to get well and overcome addiction, the sense of safety, the fellowship, and a sense of belonging with others who understand."

"Meetings are a place to celebrate the gift and acknowledge my efforts."

"Witnessing newcomers' first days/weeks of freedom is a joy to behold!"

"Opportunities to serve helps me recover value from wasted years."

"It's the program of attraction not persuasion."

"Support and acceptance. A place to be heard, respected, and healed."

101. If you've had a year or more of nicotine abstinence, do you still attend Nicotine Anonymous meetings on a regular basis?

"I attended meetings regularly for three years, then moved, so I started a new meeting."

"Yes, to serve the group. I understand I'm more likely to keep my freedom if I give back what I have gotten. In service, there is healing."

"Yes, it's one of the best ways to practice and experience my gratitude."

"There's too much to lose by not going. Meetings are my insurance."

102. How long do you expect to need meetings?

"At first I needed meetings, now I enjoy them, so I keep going."

"I work this program one day at a time and I'm committed to my recovery. I don't think I really 'need' meetings not to smoke, but I need them to stay in touch with my feelings. I have no place else to do this. I also go to meetings to carry the message because I'm grateful I don't smoke."

"I'm not concerned with how long I'll need meetings, but I am concerned with keeping my local meeting open and active for a long time."

"As long as I find them a valuable place to receive and share recovery."

"I'm a lifer."

"I will need meetings as long as I want to stay smober."

103. If you moved to a place without a Nicotine Anonymous meeting, would you start one?

"Yes, to continue both my connection to the Fellowship and my spiritual journey."

"Not at this time in my life, but possibly if I felt the urge to smoke again."

104. What are you like now?

"I am much more patient with people. I see that each of us is doing the best we can at any given moment. I'm also much more disciplined (and working on it) and more goal-oriented. I have a positive attitude most of the time when I used to be negative and cynical. I've learned that I have access to the power I need."

"My self-esteem is so much better, and hope is a reality in my life."

"More at peace, happier, healthier."

"A lot easier to get along with. People say I have mellowed out a lot."

"Looking back, I believe that I began truly living a full life after I quit smoking. It gave me the confidence to try a lot of other things. I became more active and energetic and yet more peaceful and serene. It's an incredible freedom!"

"Happy not to have the smoking paraphernalia around. Not a slave to cigarettes. No more guilt."

"I can be there for others seeking to kick the nicotine addiction. It was the toughest thing I ever did in my life."

"I certainly feel more at-one-ment with the creator. I enjoyed the questionnaire."

"What it's like now, that's what is important. I feel so much better, from the first thing in the morning, all through the day. I don't get so upset about the little things, and I seem to laugh at others who do."

"I still consider getting free of nicotine a miracle. I'm most grateful for Nicotine Anonymous and don't think I could've done it without them."

Part III
Twelve Steps of Nicotine Anonymous

1. We admitted we were powerless over nicotine—that our lives had become unmanageable.

2. Came to believe that a Power greater than ourselves could restore us to sanity.

3. Made a decision to turn our will and our lives over to the care of God, as we understood Him.

4. Made a searching and fearless moral inventory of ourselves.

5. Admitted to God, to ourselves, and to another human being the exact nature of our wrongs.

6. Were entirely ready to have God remove all these defects of character.

7. Humbly asked Him to remove our shortcomings.

8. Made a list of all persons we had harmed, and became willing to make amends to them all.

9. Made direct amends to such people wherever possible, except when to do so would injure them or others.

10. Continued to take personal inventory, and when we were wrong, promptly admitted it.

11. Sought through prayer and meditation to improve our conscious contact with God as we understood Him, praying only for knowledge of His will for us and the power to carry it out.

12. 1Having had a spiritual awakening as the result of these Steps, we tried to carry this message to other nicotine users and to practice these principles in all our affairs.

The Twelve Steps reprinted and adapted with permission of Alcoholics Anonymous World Services Inc. Permission to reprint and adapt the Twelve Steps does not mean that AA is affiliated with this program. AA is a program of recovery from alcoholism—use of the Twelve Steps in connection with programs and activities which are patterned after AA, but which address other problems does not imply otherwise.

Twelve Steps of Alcoholics Anonymous

1.   We admitted we were powerless over alcohol—that our lives had become unmanageable.
2.   Came to believe that a Power greater than ourselves could restore us to sanity.
3.   Made a decision to turn our will and our lives over to the care of God, as we understood Him.
4.   Made a searching and fearless moral inventory of ourselves.
5.   Admitted to God, to ourselves, and to another human being the exact nature of our wrongs.
6.   Were entirely ready to have God remove all these defects of character.
7.   Humbly asked Him to remove our shortcomings.
8.   Made a list of all persons we had harmed, and became willing to make amends to them all.
9.   Made direct amends to such people wherever possible, except when to do so would injure them or others.
10.   Continued to take personal inventory, and when we were wrong, promptly admitted it.
11.   Sought through prayer and meditation to improve our conscious contact with God as we understood Him, praying only for knowledge of His will for us and the power to carry it out.
12.   Having had a spiritual awakening as the result of these steps, we tried to carry this message to other alcoholics and to practice these principles in all our affairs.

STEP ONE

We admitted we were powerless over nicotine—that our lives had become unmanageable.

Step One was not an intellectual exercise. It was a feeling in our bones, in our hearts, and in our stomachs. It was a gut-wrenching coming to terms with the fact that we were hooked on a drug. We became willing for the first time to give up any notion of controlling the use of nicotine. We took a realistic look at the power nicotine had over us and we saw that its control was absolute.

It was very hard to admit anything about ourselves, much less that we were powerless over nicotine. We smoked and loved to smoke for many reasons—because it made us look sophisticated, made us feel good, reduced stress, helped us concentrate, had a calming effect, and so on. But for one reason or another, nicotine eventually stopped working: health fears, feelings of self-loathing, guilt, pressure from friends. Life as a smoker became unbearable. We began to think about stopping.

Desperately, we tried modifying our nicotine use by not using it at work or in the bedroom or in front of the children, sitting only in a particular chair while we smoked, or only when out of doors. We switched brands, used tar reducing cigarette holders, smoked only "natural cigarettes," smoked only at certain times of the day, with certain people, at special events. Then we began to consult the experts. We sought help from physicians, hypnotherapists, psychiatrists, acupuncturists, self-help books, and countless smoking cessation programs. Sometimes we were able to quit, but we could not stay quit. Nothing worked.

Deeply demoralized, we turned to Nicotine Anonymous as one more possible solution. To our great surprise, we found people who were not using nicotine because they had admitted they could not stop. They accepted their utter lack of control over nicotine, and offered us support by inviting us to join them and do the same. There was support from the group; and as the use of the pronoun "we" throughout the Steps suggests, the process of recovering from nicotine addiction was not and is not a journey that one travels alone.

We realized that we were truly addicts and that we used nicotine for the same reason that alcoholics drank—because we could not stop. Left to our own devices we would continue to smoke, continue to destroy our bodies, suppress our feelings, and alienate our families, lovers, and friends.

Joining Nicotine Anonymous involved acknowledging that we alone could not solve our problem with nicotine. After the countless attempts to control our "habit," it was almost a relief to give up and seek help. We learned about turning the tables, surrendering, and admitting our powerlessness. We accepted our total lack of control over nicotine.

We realized that using nicotine was more than a bad habit; rather, it was a symptom that our lives were out of control and unmanageable. The destructive aspects of our addiction went far beyond the obvious damage we did to our bodies. The more we looked at the role nicotine played in our lives, the more we realized how much it controlled us. Nicotine determined when we would take breaks, where we would eat, who our friends, lovers, and associates were, how we spent our free time. We never went anywhere or did anything without first checking our supply. Yet we went to great lengths to conceal our addiction from others and ourselves. We used mouthwash, room spray, smoke-eating machines, to name but a few. Many of us even began to hide when we used—avoiding the presence of friends and loved ones, or sneaking a cigarette in the toilet stall at work. There was no way to hide, and the very attempt was a lie. Our lives were lies. They were out of control—unmanageable.

Understanding and experiencing both parts of Step One, that we are powerless over nicotine *and* that our lives had become unmanageable was the beginning. We were ready to take Step Two.

STEP TWO

Came to believe that a Power greater than ourselves could restore us to sanity.

In Step One, we admitted our powerlessness. For some of us, this was a devastating admission. We looked back at our years of nicotine addiction and at all our attempts to quit. Every attempt had failed. We realized that we could not stop. Neither self-recrimination, will power, nor analysis of our situation helped. We felt like failures. We asked, "Why can't we quit when everyone else can?"

Now at Step Two we began to find answers to our questions. Having admitted our own powerlessness, we began to open ourselves to finding a source of power greater than ourselves, greater than our addiction. Out of the despair and without understanding why, there came an awareness of an alternative. We accepted the possibility of hope.

Those of us who had a positive spiritual connection looked to God, as we understood God, as the alternative, as the source of hope. For those of us who had developed a skeptical attitude about religion, coming to believe in a Higher Power was no small task. We found that our original conception of a Power greater than ourselves had failed us. We rebelled against attempts to convince us of fixed ideas about God. We resisted involvement in an unquestioning faith.

Acknowledging our skepticism, we learned that we didn't even have to have a definition of God or a Power greater than ourselves. We could just act as if we believed, trusting when we did not know or understand. "Coming to believe" was a process. It had nothing to do with logic, reason, certainty, or figuring things out. Instead, it had to do with our own personal convictions, with an open mind, flexibility, and a willingness to allow something good to happen to ourselves.

With our openness, we examined the phrase "restore us to sanity." We had always thought of ourselves as fairly sane. But how could we have thought that, when 20, 40, 60 or more times a day, we continued to smoke when we knew it was killing us?

At first, the notion of insanity seemed dramatic, especially to apply it to ourselves. We listened at meetings to others' stories.

Hearing their tales of dangerous midnight cigarette runs, plucking butts out of gutters, garbage cans and public ashtrays, and smoking through tracheotomy tubes, caused us to remember similar behavior of our own. We saw our own insanity—repeating the same actions over and over, expecting the results to be different.

Admitting our insanity around nicotine would have left us in despair if our only solution had been our own will power. Left on our own, there was no way out. Somebody, something—some *Power*—had to help.

We saw others' success, and we listened when they suggested that we suspend our rational thinking and give this other Power an opportunity to work in our lives. As we began to hear what they were saying, there was a sense of hope. We were not alone after all. This Power and our connection to it, and to other people was the doorway to a life free from nicotine.

STEP THREE

Made a decision to turn our will and our lives over to the care of God
as we understood Him.

In Steps One and Two, we accepted our personal powerlessness, the unmanageability of our lives, the need for faith in a Power greater than ourselves, and the reality of our own insane actions.

Our addiction continued to fight for its life. The cravings still possessed us, and we were feeling an unbelievable variety of uncomfortable and awful feelings: anger, rage, shame, longing, self-loathing, and despair. We lost our best friend. We were alone, facing the rest of our lives without our drug.

Now we came to a Step where it was suggested that we make a decision. We needed to decide that we were no longer in charge and that we needed help. This decision greatly contradicted what we had been taught. How many times had we heard that we should be able to use willpower to rid ourselves of the nasty little habit of smoking? From childhood, we were taught to rely on ourselves. We learned that no one was going to do it for us. We knew that if we wanted it done right we should do it ourselves.

Unfortunately, relying on ourselves proved ineffective in dealing with our addiction to nicotine. It didn't keep us from smoking. We found it extremely difficult to ask for help. We associated help with dependence and weakness. We weren't interested in being told how to run our lives.

Gradually, in meetings, through listening to others or by reading, we began to see that what we had proudly viewed as self-reliance was really arrogance, rebelliousness, defiance, and denial. We could also see that these attitudes were really unhealthy for us. With this awareness, we saw that asking for help was an act of strength, not weakness. We understood that by being humble, we could allow something kind and powerful to help us. We needed this understanding in order to decide to ask for the help we so desperately needed.

We surrendered. Through surrender came the willingness to try anything, including letting ourselves be helped by something good and wonderful. As Bill Wilson, who first wrote about these Twelve Steps said, "Our whole trouble had been the misuse of will power. We had tried to bombard our problems with it instead of attempting to bring it into agreement with God's intention for us."

Our goal was to make contact with a Higher Power—one that would help us to change ourselves and our lives. We found that as we made this contact, we were able to make a decision to turn our will and our lives over to the care of our own God. We found support. We discovered a new sense of well-being of body, emotion, and spirit.

We found that by keeping close to our Higher Power, we experienced the Third Step in action. We became less and less interested in ourselves, our little plans and designs. More and more we became interested in seeing what we could contribute to life, leaving it to our Higher Power to help take care of us. As we felt the new Power flow in, we enjoyed peace of mind, discovered we could face life successfully, felt our Higher Power, and began to lose our fear of yesterday, today, and tomorrow. We sought freedom from self-will and ego, and the wisdom to recognize our Higher Power's will for us. We did this in many ways, including repeating the following:

Third Step Prayer

Relieve me of the bondage of self.

Help me abandon myself to the spirit.

Move me to do good in this world and show kindness.

*Help me to overcome and avoid anger, resentment,
jealousy and any other kind
of negative thinking today.*

Help me to help those who suffer.

*Keep me alert with courage to face life and not
withdraw from it, not to insulate myself
from all pain whereby I insulate myself
from love as well.*

*Free me from fantasy and fear. Inspire and direct my
thinking today; let it be divorced from self pity,
dishonesty and self-seeking motives.*

*Show me the way of patience, tolerance,
kindliness and love.*

*I pray for all of those to whom I've been unkind
and ask that they are granted
the same peace that I seek.*

Through trust in our Higher Power, we found that we were taken care of in surprising and simple ways. This gave us new confidence and an increasing faith. Our victory over our own difficulties encouraged us to continue, and we became an example for others as well.

STEP FOUR

Made a searching and fearless
moral inventory of ourselves.

The word "inventory" comes from a Latin word which means to come upon or discover. Among the definitions of "moral" is one that means to make the distinction between right and wrong conduct. These literal definitions were good guidelines to keep in mind while doing Step Four.

Step Four was a daring look deep into the mirror, writing down what we saw. By means of looking in the mirror, we attempted to discover what behaviors and attitudes worked and what did not work in the way we conducted our lives. The purpose of the exercise was to let us recognize and sort through the chaos of our lives. By taking an inventory, we got a clear picture of the disorganization and unmanageability that had held us captive in our addiction.

Our inventory also included our good qualities, our assets, which, when we first stopped using nicotine may have been almost impossible for us to see. As an aspect of self-care, it was important to humbly acknowledge these personal assets as supportive strengths. These strengths were often helpful when addressing behaviors and attitudes we needed to change or improve.

According to the language of Step Four, our moral inventory was to be "fearless." Yet, most of us were afraid as we stood on the threshold of this Step because of the negativism that filled our lives. We were deeply frightened of taking the hard look at ourselves that was called for by the Fourth Step. We knew ourselves as bad people, failures, losers, and imposters and we really did not want to look all of that in the face.

But we were on the way to being done with those self-destructive notions. Reflecting back over Steps One, Two and Three, we realized that we had the positive energy and guidance of a Higher Power to help us take a hard look. We recalled we were no longer alone.

We heard others in Nicotine Anonymous share their experiences with the Fourth Step and learned that they discovered they were not as wretched as they had feared. Trusting in the experience of others, and with the help of our Higher Power, we found the courage to honestly inventory ourselves. We dared to surrender to our Higher Power and let ourselves be guided through Step Four.

Step Four tells us that the moral inventory should be "searching." This means thorough. There was no magic measuring device that could tell us how much, how deep, how long we were to look at ourselves. But the stocktaking was to be searching, to the very best of our ability at the time.

There was no such thing as a good inventory versus a bad inventory; there was only the best possible inventory we could make. The best possible was that which could be done with total honesty, humility, candor, surrender, and willingness. It should be simple and thorough. The important thing was to do it.

Many of us experienced some pain doing our Fourth Step inventory. But it was important to remember that the purpose of the inventory was not to cause pain. Rather, we were trying to get a handle on how we had been living our lives. We wanted to list what worked and what did not work for us, so that we could identify and stop the useless patterns of our past.

We wanted to know how we got stuck in our past so we could find our way out of that trap, so we could find freedom from our old selves and freedom from nicotine. We were getting free of yesterday so we could live today, each day, one day at a time.

Just as there was no correct definition of a "good" inventory, there was also no absolute "right" way to take stock. We found writing it down was basic and necessary. Putting our inventory on paper made it more real and made it easier for us to be certain that we had been as searching and fearless as possible. Anything that popped up we wrote down. The goal was thoroughness. There was nothing that did not belong on the list. It was easy. If it came to mind, it went on the list.

One way to get started was to answer the questions in the Nicotine Anonymous Questionnaire that appears in Part II of these materials. The Questionnaire gave good insight into what we were trying to get from nicotine. Patterns emerged in the responses. Ideas cropped up. Those patterns and ideas were explored further.

Another option is to use the *Step Study Workbook* section for Step Four. A member (often with the help of her or his sponsor) reads the text and then discusses the questions. Some members may even choose to use the entire Workbook as their "searching and fearless" approach to the Fourth Step.

A third approach was to think about the things we felt good about and the things we felt bad about in the past, and how we felt about them as we wrote. We wrote them down and we asked ourselves questions like these about them:

- Why do I feel that way?
- Who else was affected by this?
- Is this part of a pattern?
- Am I responsible for what happened then?
- Do I go on repeating it? How?

We wrote down all the things we felt bad about. We analyzed them: where they came from, what they did to us, why we hung onto them, how they affected those around us. We asked for help from our Higher Power to really look in the mirror and confront them.

We did the same with the things we felt good about, starting with what we already had accomplished. We were clean; we were not using nicotine anymore. We continued to think about the positives. We let ourselves be guided by a Higher Power into exploring them as far as possible.

Others found that a fourth approach to the inventory was to start with lists of persons, institutions, principles, or events we felt played important roles in our lives. We then explored what their influence or effect was on us.

That process of exploration involved looking at the people and events that led to past fears, resentments, self-loathing, or to our staying in situations long after they stopped being useful. We sought to find who or what got us to feel and think negatively. Much of it happened early in life. For many of us, it was important to go back as far as we could remember, even if the details were hazy. Much of it amazed us. Some of it seemed small and petty, but if it came up at all, it was important and we wrote it down. Whatever it was, we advanced the cause of getting free from our past by getting it down on paper.

For those of us who found that making these lists was too vague, a fifth approach was easier. We wrote a totally honest personal history, which let us see how we were led into our addiction. From our understanding of what happened, we got a better picture of where and why and how we were damaged, and how that damage had influenced our behavior since.

It was not necessary, or perhaps even possible, to understand where the autobiography was leading us while we were writing it. In other words, sometimes it was not until we were finished writing down our own life story that we were able to go back to the beginning and see the individual events in a bigger perspective. But, with the advantage of the bigger picture, what before seemed like a dumb little thing, suddenly became a significant part of a large, clear pattern.

Many of us who had done a Fourth Step in another 12-step program found it necessary to rethink our inventories, giving special attention to the unique impact of nicotine addiction on our lives. For example, we found that nicotine blocked our feelings and our interactions with other human beings and the world around us. Whether we were hiding behind our smoke screen or blowing smoke at others, we crippled ourselves in ways that seemed to be unique or especially aggravated by nicotine. Thus, our recovery from other substances, as well as from nicotine, got a special boost when we reconsidered our previous inventories.

The Fourth Step allowed us to see ourselves clearly and without so much judgment. The picture it provided helped eliminate the fear that we would discover we were really awful. The Fourth Step allowed us to feel that we were ordinary people more connected to ourselves and others.

STEP FIVE

Admitted to God, to ourselves, and to another human being the exact nature of our wrongs.

In making the Fourth Step inventory, we put into an organized form all the chaos, confusion, and trouble of our past. We made an extensive review of our life. Now what?

Step Five was getting rid of the old stuff. It was the biggest spring housecleaning of our life, and its aim was to get rid of all the cobwebs, dust balls and other junk and debris that accumulated during the long winter of our addiction. It was getting into position to replace the old garbage with positive new thoughts and ways. It was getting free—getting free of what had not worked, getting free of what had trapped us in the deathly grips of nicotine for so long. It was taking out the trash.

The success of cleaning out the old garbage in Step Five depended on having dug it out and put it in piles in Step Four. It was not enough, however, just to have written the inventory. Some of our old stuff was on the list, but buried—swept under the carpet. We knew it was there, but we hoped that nobody else would find it. Nonetheless, if we really wanted to clean house, the old dirt could not stay hidden under the rug.

Thus, the objective of Step Five was to admit what we had found. We may even have found that we had wrongly denied or had not acknowledged certain good qualities about ourselves. We made a private admission to ourselves. To make certain that we were not cheating, we also admitted everything to our Higher Power. It mattered not that a wiser God already knew. It was our act of admission and humility that mattered.

Step Five also required us to share our inventory with another human being. For many of us, this was even more frightening than the admission to our Higher Power. Admitting all of the details of our past torments to another person was so concrete, so real, and so humbling. It required swallowing our pride.

Humbleness was the core of Step Five. Becoming humble was what it was all about. The Fifth Step was about getting conscious of our shortcomings. It was about becoming modest and not proud or arrogant. It was about not pretending and not running and hiding anymore. It was about getting real and becoming very human.

The Fifth Step involved sharing intimate personal details with a trusted person and getting humble in the process. We shrank down to our core and to who we really were. Through sharing our deepest secrets with another person, we opened ourselves up. In that way, we made it possible to be healed from our addiction to nicotine.

Becoming honest was a way to get free to be who we were. We stripped naked and stood in all our bare glory without any of the disguises that had hidden us when we were nicotine addicts. When we admitted to ourselves, to our Higher Power, and to another human being who we were, we became free of our past sufferings and free to love ourselves and to stop trying to destroy ourselves.

We were very careful in selecting the other person with whom we chose to open ourselves up during the Fifth Step. The object of the experience was candor and honesty, trust, and openness. The other person had to be someone who would allow us to feel as absolutely free and open as possible. For some of us, it was our sponsor or another person from Nicotine Anonymous. For others, it was clergy, a therapist, or a friend. Whomever we selected, it was someone we thought would let us be totally honest and open.

As we candidly shared our secrets, we discovered that we were not as terrible as we thought. Somehow, in the process of describing "the worst thing we've ever done," the terribleness of it all was lessened. The most terrible things really were not so awful after all.

We also discovered that all of our fears, troubles, and supposed shortcomings were not unique. In the process of opening ourselves up, our confidants frequently shared with us many of the very same things that we were telling them. We discovered that our troubles and tribulations were just part of the human condition. We were not awful. We were humbled to realize that we were normal—and just very human.

Step Five. Cleaning up our lives. Gratefully letting go of the past to get ready for the present. We can have a new spiritual awareness of our membership in the human race and let that be quite all right.

STEP SIX

Were entirely ready to have God remove all these defects of character.

Before we began Step Six, many of us found it useful to meditate and consider our work thus far. If we had been thorough, we had done a great deal of work, some of it very difficult.

In our meditation, we reflected on the first three Steps. Once again, we accepted our powerlessness, reiterated our faith, and recommitted to our decision to surrender to the care of our Higher Power. We realized we had deepened our understanding of the process of recovery. After concluding that the examination of our lives in Steps Four and Five was as complete a job as we were capable of making, we were ready to take Step Six.

Step Six is a transition Step. It is where we really began to change. We needed to consider what this change meant to us. Through Steps Four and Five we came to know ourselves more deeply than we ever had. We came face to face with what had worked for us and what had not, as well as with our effective and ineffective traits. We came to understand that there were reasons for our behavior. In Step Six we examined the reasons and our motivation for our behavior. With this additional knowledge, we began to consider healthier ways of meeting our needs. In other words, we were ready to have God remove our defects, or ineffective traits of character.

We saw that each of our character defects was two-sided. Each had the potential to hurt us, as we saw in Step Four, but each could also bring us pleasure, or a sense of acceptance, or perhaps the means of avoiding stress, fear, or pain. Now, we learned how to incorporate pleasure into our lives in healthier ways. We came to see how our need for acceptance could be met without injury to ourselves. We realized that, once acknowledged and accepted, stress and fear could be greatly diminished. Our newly found faith did not explain away pain, which we accepted as an integral part of life, but it did give us the courage to face it, and to feel it, instead of using nicotine to stuff it or avoid it.

In working Step Six, we found it helpful to recognize the benefits and penalties we got from acting out our character defects. We began to understand why we did certain things, and what it was we were trying to get from the process. We learned to recognize that, in the process, we also got many things we did not want.

We realized, for instance, that our overly-judgmental approach to life worked as a way of boosting our own sense of self-worth and helped us cover up our feelings of inadequacy or fear. At the same time, we came to understand that this approach kept us separate from those we were judging. It locked us into a false sense of superiority. It deprived us of honesty in relationships with others.

Once we understood what we really were attempting to accomplish, we developed new methods for getting the same results in ways that were not self-destructive. In our pursuit of authentic self-worth, we acknowledged our own positive attributes and built on them. We were no longer concerned with how we were perceived by others. We refused to allow our self-worth to be determined by others' opinions.

In our attempt to deal with our feelings of inadequacy and fear, we came to realize that these were normal human feelings. We understood and accepted our limitations. Sometimes we were not old enough. Sometimes we were not young enough. We were not supermen or superwomen. We could not do everything. Furthermore, we live in a sometimes dangerous world and fear is a legitimate emotion.

Once we realized that these feelings were acceptable, we focused on them in a different way. We examined what it was that made us feel inadequate. We learned what it was that frightened us. Armed with the information these efforts provided, and with the help of our Higher Power, we could prepare for situations in new ways that reduced or eliminated feelings of fear and inadequacy.

When we came to understand the concept of being "ready" to have our character defects removed, we were able to consider being "entirely" ready. We became willing to let go and to change. The notion of "entirely" was a goal we worked toward.

We were comforted by the thought that we sought progress and not perfection. We thought back to the Third Step when we decided to turn our will and our lives over to the care of God, as we understood God. We confirmed that we meant our *total* will and our *entire* life.

In Step Six we moved from one period of our life to another. We learned the difference between holding on to the past and letting it go. We began to learn to stop living in the pain of yesterday and to start living in the pleasure of today. We were now truly ready, with a clear conscience, to ask our Higher Power for help.

STEP SEVEN

Humbly asked Him
to remove our shortcomings.

In the middle of the Twelve Steps, after the relief of admitting our powerlessness over nicotine and a searching moral inventory, we put ourselves on the line and asked God to remove our shortcomings. We asked our Higher Power to take away the roadblocks we had constructed which kept us unhappy and afraid and incapable of meeting life without our drug, nicotine.

The Step itself required only that we humbly ask God to remove our shortcomings. Let's first think about the word "humbly." Some of us were put off by this word because it so closely resembles the words "humiliate" and "humiliation." These words seemed too negative. We came to understand that the word "humbly" did not mean debasing ourselves. What it meant was seeing our proper place in the grand scheme of things. We acknowledged our Higher Power as a higher, more complete, more encompassing entity than ourselves. We saw that our Higher Power was more, and that we were less. But we were not less in a bad or pejorative sense. We were less in respect to our Higher Power. This is the correct understanding of humility. It is the acceptance of our very true and very human limitations.

Accepting our ultimate humanity and our human limitations is different from acknowledging our shortcomings, which we had done in Step Four. As we progressed from Step Four through Step Six we identified, admitted, considered, and began to psychologically detach from these shortcomings. We called them "inventory" in Step Four, "wrongs" in Step Five, and "character defects" in Step Six. Whatever the label for these ineffective behavior patterns, we realized that our addiction itself was the prime example. We also realized that the guilt and shame we felt about our shortcomings was part of the reason we used nicotine. As we accept these shortcomings as normal human failings, our extreme responses to basic instincts, we acknowledge our imperfection. We realize our previous behavior patterns have not worked for us or for others. We see that they have made our lives unmanageable.

Reflecting back on Step Two, we came to believe that a Power greater than ourselves could restore us to sanity. Here is where we ask that Higher Power to do so. Having explored various alternatives to our shortcomings, we are now ready to take the Seventh Step.

Some of us took this Step by saying the following words, *"My Higher Power, I place myself in your hands and humbly ask that my character defects be lifted from me so that I may help others. Please grant me willingness, courage, and strength so that through my actions I may reflect your love and wisdom. Amen."*

We have found that there are many ways to take this Step. What works best for many of us is to pray aloud in a quiet room where we can hear what we are saying and reflect on it as we say it. In bed, upon awakening and before getting up, works well. On our knees works, too. The important thing is to say our words. They can form the basis of a worthwhile daily meditation alone, or together with other prayers or affirmations.

We have found that these words can do more than get our day off to a strong start. They can take the edge off situations and feelings long enough for us to forget the urge to use nicotine. When we think about the many times our resolve not to use nicotine has crumbled in the face of tough situations and intense emotions, we recognize our limitations. Step Seven reinforces our sense of powerlessness and our willingness to ask for help.

Asking for help was often difficult for us. We wanted to believe that we were totally self-sufficient and independent. Our willingness to see ourselves as needing help, which was an essential part of the First Step, left us with a feeling of emptiness. It was when we started to work the Second Step that this emptiness was filled with our faith in a Power greater than ourselves. To our great surprise we found that our decision to surrender our will, and our willingness to ask for help from a Higher Power, or even from our fellow human beings, was a liberating experience. Not only did it remove the unrealistic pressure we had placed on ourselves, but we also began to make progress. In fact, our very definition of the word progress began to change. We leave it up to our Higher Power to remove these shortcomings. We learn that whether and when they will be removed is up to our Higher Power, and not up to us.

As we increase our conscious contact with our Higher Power, we also hope to increase our knowledge of our Higher Power's will for us. Perhaps in this way we will come to understand why our Higher Power leaves us the capacity to behave ineffectively. After all we have made a decision to turn our will and our lives over to the care of a Higher Power as we each may come to understand.

Nicotine is cunning, baffling, powerful, and patient. We are never free from our addiction. By working Step Seven and reciting the Seventh Step prayer, we ask for *willingness, courage, and strength* from a Power greater than ourselves so that through our actions we may reflect our Higher Power's *love and wisdom.*

STEP EIGHT

Made a list of all persons we had harmed, and became willing to make amends to them all.

We continued our journey toward our one-day-at-a-time reprieve from nicotine addiction in the Eighth Step by preparing ourselves to make amends to all of those we had harmed and by becoming willing to make amends to them. The purpose of this Step is to achieve freedom from guilt over our past actions and interactions with other people.

We define "harm" as any form of physical, mental, emotional, or spiritual damage that our actions may have caused others. If we kept our Fourth Step inventory, we may already have a list of people with whom we have had negative interactions. Many of us used this as our starting point for Step Eight. We surveyed the whole area of personal relationships and searched our memories for the people to whom we had given offense. The more recent and damaging the relationship, the quicker the memory surfaced. We went back through our lives, asking for guidance and direction from our Higher Power and put the names of these people on paper.

While preparing this list of amends due, the addict within sometimes attempted to color our thinking with all sorts of rationalizations. This seemed especially true if we prematurely anticipated the actual making of amends that takes place in Step Nine. Step Eight suggests that we make a list and become willing. It is not the direct amend-making Step. We stayed in the Eighth Step and worked the Ninth Step in its proper turn.

As we looked on the list of people to whom amends were due, we put out of our minds the wrongs, perceived or real, that others may have done to us. Our purpose was not to evaluate the behavior of others but to look only at our part of the interaction. We had to keep in mind that we were here to clear away the wreckage of our past, not to make others accountable for their wrongdoings.

Some instances of harm were directly related to our nicotine use, especially if we had been inconsiderate or selfish in our addictive behaviors around family, friends, or co-workers. We looked at the impact of our second-hand smoke or spit tobacco on those who had been in our presence, remembering both the individuals we knew and all the strangers who crossed our path. We also looked at the pollution we added to the environment with the cigarette butts or spit tobacco that we left on city streets and mountain trails. We looked at the subtle harm we may have caused in our relationships by the ways we had used cigarettes as a barrier to intimacy, creating a true smoke screen to maintain an emotional distance between us and those in our lives. If our nicotine use in any form caused harm, such as cigarette burns or tobacco wad stains, we listed the restitution that was due.

We then made note of harm we did that was not directly related to our nicotine addiction. This included those we harmed due to our anger, fears, pride, and other personality traits that we had explored in our Fourth Step.

Some of us found it valuable to place ourselves on our amends list. So much of the damage caused by the use of nicotine and the defects accompanying our addiction, such as isolation and low self-esteem, were of greatest harm to our own bodies and lives.

We found that we made little progress in our new way of living until we backtracked and made an accurate and unsparing survey of the wreckage of our past. We were not able to develop the best possible relations with every person we knew until we "came clean" to ourselves, to God, and to another human being, and now—to the people involved in our tornado-ridden path.

There was a long period of reconstruction ahead. A remorseful grumbling or mumbling that we were sorry was not going to work. A sponsor or trusted friend could help us achieve the objectivity in preparing to go to these people. We did not hesitate to seek advice from our fellows and we asked our Higher Power for the willingness to proceed to Step Nine.

STEP NINE

Made direct amends to such people wherever possible, except when to do so would injure them or others.

The Eighth and Ninth Steps were our effort to bring ourselves into harmony with the world around us. We carried out the housecleaning that, so far, had been essentially inward and reflective.

We made amends, one at a time, with care and compassion. Taking a name from our Eighth Step list, we reflected on the nature of the harm done to that person. Now was the time to try our hardest to put ourselves in the other person's shoes concerning our past interaction with him or her. What was it like to be on the receiving end of our poor behavior? How was that person's view of the world or personality altered as a result of what we had done? Did our actions cause another to lose trust in people in general? We asked ourselves how we might have had a negative influence or impact on others.

Usually, this reflection stirred an eagerness to set matters right. Seeing things from another's perspective conjured up a sudden and uneasy awareness of the pain or disappointment our actions had caused. Although these feelings made our amends heartfelt, we could not let them lead to morbid reflection and remorse. That kept us from the positive path of action that is the focus of this Step.

The best antidote for morbidity was a calm and open manner and straightforward attitude. We put our newly found awareness of the nature of the harm done into the background and, praying for guidance, asked our Higher Power for the best way to amend the injury. We asked around the fellowship and found other people who had dealt with similar amends. We consulted our sponsors. We trusted that our Higher Power would direct our thinking as we proceeded.

Contacting the person harmed, we explained that our addiction to nicotine was in abeyance through our practice of the spiritual program of Nicotine Anonymous. The program stresses that we put right the wrongs we had done in the past and repair relationships with the people we had harmed. And that is why we were here.

We went on to explain in appropriate detail the harm we felt we had done. While this did not instantly remedy matters, its long-term effect was powerful. If we had caused a material loss to the person we offered to make restitution. However, most often the harm was emotional and spiritual in nature. Where emotional damage had been done, we apologized and stated that we were now trying to live honestly and in harmony with others.

Saying we were sorry was often not enough. Sometimes the person we were talking with was skeptical, especially if we had remorsefully made apologies in the past, promised changed behavior, and then simply gone back to our old ways. Changing our actions and making living amends was necessary. Living our amends means acting and doing the healthy, loving things to others that we had previously promised. Apologizing for past negative actions and stopping them in the present was not enough; we now had to take positive personal actions toward others and strive toward establishing the correct relations with everyone we come into contact with. Long-term reconstruction of relationships comes through consistent behavior over time.

We also remembered to take our inventory and not the other person's. We talked of what we had done, not of what the other person had done. Even if we firmly believed the other person had contributed to 90% of the problem and we had caused only 10% of the problem, we talked only about the 10% we were responsible for. We were only there to clean up our side of the street. If the other person, in the spirit of reconciliation, talked of their actions, we simply listened and thanked them for their comments. We did not judge, criticize, or argue.

The person being approached may have responded with anger and not forgiveness. However, we did not try to make them see our point of view. We accepted their feelings and expressed that we hoped in the future they could forgive us, and left it at that and in the care of our Higher Power.

We made sure we did not make amends in any way that would cause further harm or pain to the person affected. We did not reveal secrets that felt good for us to confess but which might cause pain to the other person. We avoided emotional dumping that selfishly gave emotional release solely to ourselves.

Often our self-centered behavior caused discomfort or harm to groups of people or to individuals who had passed through our lives anonymously. These people had endured our cigarette smoke in confined spaces like elevators, or saw our discarded cigarette butts along a pristine mountain trail. In these cases many of us found that we needed to make amends to the world in general. We sought ways to repay the world for the harm we had done. This could take the form of volunteer work with environmental groups, service in Nicotine Anonymous, or other less formal activities that are of service to people.

In certain cases we could not make direct amends to the people we had harmed. Perhaps they had died or we had lost touch with them, or they refused to see us. In these cases we found that the "amends to the world in general" concept worked. If we had been a poor daughter or son to a now deceased parent, we took actions toward others who were in similar situations to our parents; we adopted, helped and loved a senior citizen. If we could not communicate to the person harmed, we made a living amends to someone with whom we could interact.

In our explanation of what we were doing we usually mentioned Nicotine Anonymous and how it had brought us to the current situation. However, our purpose was not to explain our program or our newly found spirituality. If talk of program and spirituality made others uncomfortable we did not press those issues but got down to the business of making amends.

It takes time to make amends. We learned patience through the process. It takes courage and a willingness to proceed in principle on a course of action when we cannot predict the outcome. We learned to plan our course of action, to carry it out with determination, and to accept whatever result it brought. We proceeded in the knowledge that this worked not only to keep us free of nicotine, but also to help us achieve a new rapport with others and to reduce our sense of loneliness and isolation.

Having done the best we could to restore the emotional and material security we disrupted in those we harmed, we began to see the world in a new light. We knew now that our individual actions radiate more broadly in the world than we had ever imagined. As a result of our admission of our powerlessness over nicotine, we came at last to understand the real point of our power. In this pursuit, we gradually discovered that our knowledge and tolerance of others had increased and our place in humanity had become, for the first time in our lives, truly comfortable.

STEP TEN

Continued to take personal inventory and when we were wrong promptly admitted it.

During the first nine Steps, we concentrated on identifying and giving up the problems of the past while acknowledging our assets and good qualities. We turned our will and life over to the care of God/Higher Power as we each have come to understand. We set the stage for moving into the rest of our life with joy and freedom.

Step Ten helps us stay in check on our progress in this new life. On an ongoing basis, we examine our daily actions and interactions with ourselves and others. We identify any problem areas in terms of our behavior on each day. We make amends to those we might have offended, and thank God and ourselves for our successes.

This Step helps us to be right with ourselves, others, and our Higher Power. Healthy behavior and healthy attitudes are important to recovery from nicotine dependence. Through this Step we are given the opportunity to keep our commitment to strive for openness, honesty, humility, and love for ourselves and others. It is our path to peace and serenity. It clears the path to closeness with ourselves, others, and with our Higher Power. Step Ten helps us maintain behavior essential in remaining abstinent from the use of nicotine.

The Tenth Step asks us to continually be aware of how our actions influence the lives of those around us. This helps us maintain an awareness that we are as important to other people's recovery as they are to ours. We learn to be responsible to the values we cherish in relationships with others, such as openness, honesty, and truthfulness. Step Ten provides us with the direct knowledge that these values are our guides to our behavior.

Working this Step daily provides us with continuous feedback on our progress and on our stumbling blocks. It may reveal to us just how often we have to make amends to others before we are willing to change our behavior. We begin to see our resistance to change, openness, honesty, and humility. We are able to see the struggle we have inside, especially when we don't want to admit our wrongs or apologize for an act that hurt someone else. Strength can come from acknowledging our resistance and may provide us with the humility that may be necessary in asking for help.

The Tenth Step helps us keep our side of the street clean. It is a great reminder to keep the focus on ourselves. When we can do that, we are generally more assured that we are still on course. Our faith is strengthened that we will receive the promises of sanity and serenity.

STEP ELEVEN

**Sought through prayer and meditation
to improve our conscious contact with God**
as we understood Him, **praying only
for knowledge of His will for us
and the power to carry that out.**

Our lives have been spent creating distance between ourselves
and the peace inside us. We have crafted clouds of smoky fog
between ourselves and our Higher Power to the degree that we
no longer can see our Higher Power. Step Eleven is what we do
to clean up the fog and see ourselves and our relationship to God
in a clear and serene light. It strengthens the connection between
us and our Higher Power. Breaking the Step down into smaller
components may help in examining its importance.

"Sought through prayer and meditation ..."
Each person is free to come to his/her own understanding of what
prayer means. Prayer is viewed by some as a "heightened
perception of intuition." Others see it as talking with their higher
self, or talking to God. Some people already established a form of
prayer before they got into the program. These people perhaps
didn't have a problem initiating contact with a Higher Power.
Others find it difficult, if not impossible, to pray. The important
thing is to do whatever we need to strengthen the bond between
ourselves and a power greater than ourselves. People who have
difficulty praying can also ask for help from fellow Nicotine
Anonymous members. A sponsor can be especially helpful at this
stage by sharing experience, strength, and hope.

There are no correct or incorrect prayers, ways of praying, or
places to pray—but it is crucial that we sincerely seek our Higher
Power's will and guidance. Whatever works, works, and is not to
be judged by others. Some people only feel they are praying if
they are on their knees, humbling themselves before their Higher
Power. Others pray while they work, jog, or drive their cars. It
proves useful to begin our day with some kind of prayer, asking
God for guidance and to direct our thinking and actions towards
God's ends. At night, before going to sleep, we take some time to

mentally list all the things we have to be thankful for today—one more day of being nicotine-free, our health, friends, loved ones, jobs, homes, etc. We can reflect on the changes that have occurred in our lives since we stopped using nicotine and started letting go of egotistical, self-willed attachments.

In the past, many of us prayed to God only to ask for specific things or results. Now we ask ourselves, "How can I request a specific outcome when I ultimately cannot always know what is good for me or someone else?" Acceptance, not control, is the key. As long as we ask for specifics, we are not letting go and letting God. By adopting an open attitude and listening to our Higher Power we are given far more than we ever dreamed. Instead of asking for what we want and what we think we need, we focus on offering ourselves to our Higher Power ready to perform actions as spiritually guided.

As with prayer, meditation techniques vary widely and each person can find his/her own way. Meditation leads us to become still, open, and receptive. It helps us go inside ourselves, to be quiet, and to empty ourselves so our Higher Power can come in and fill us up. Sitting peacefully in front of a candle can help to produce a state of inner calm and single-mindedness. So can sitting alone on an isolated beach, under a tree in the mountains, or in a chair at a kitchen table. One way to begin to meditate is to simply sit still and focus on our breath as it moves in and out. Let the diaphragm do the work—just observe what happens. Another tool some people use is to visualize God in the heart. Let God expand and take over the body, the room, and the world.

"... to improve our conscious contact with God ..."

Whatever we do for our Eleventh Step, it is most important that we do something. This Step is an action Step. While many of us start by doing Step Eleven for a few minutes a day, we find through experience that it is possible to have a connection with our Higher Power at all moments of the day and night. While this is very difficult, it is possible. Many find that the more contact they have with their Higher Power, the more serene they become.

Some individuals have discovered useful tools for gaining a more constant contact with a Power greater than oneself, and here are a few:

- Ask your Higher Power for help when making decisions.
- Perform every action as though it were a gift to God.
- Come up with an image of a Higher Power (i.e. candle flame, ocean) and imagine that image as much as possible.
- Think of ourselves as a tool in the hands of God.
- Repeat program slogans to ourselves.
- Think of ourselves as a cell in the body of our Higher Power, or a star in the body of the universe.

"... as we understood Him ..."

We are guided to find, know, and understand a God/ Higher Power that works for us. There are no rules for this. A Higher Power can be an inner voice, nature, other people, or a rock. The program can work only if we are free to explore our individual paths and realize the experience of a Higher Power we need for today.

It is useful to remember that finding an understanding of a Higher Power is a process, not an event. We have our whole lives to search for this Power, for meaning, for answers. There is no hurry. Today is enough. Our Higher Power helps us to find what we need, and helps us to do what we need to do.

"... praying only for knowledge of His will for us ..."

How do we know what our Higher Power's will is for us? Sometimes it can be easier to think about what our Higher Power's will is *not*. It is not our Higher Power's will for us to continue using nicotine. Using nicotine drew us away from our Higher Power. Quitting the use of nicotine began to move us closer to our Higher Power.

If we concentrate on praying for and performing God's will, our own petty desires and egotistical wants start to diminish. We become more serene and flow with our own essential nature. We find that the fruits of our actions are God's concern and not ours. We become more involved with action and less concerned with results. Life is easier when we get our egos out of the way and firmly establish our minds and hearts in our Higher Power.

"... and the power to carry that out."

The last thing the Eleventh Step suggests is that we pray for the power to carry out God's will. Some see this power as willingness, strength, acceptance, courage, and commitment. Others put all these things together and call it faith. Faith does not mean stupidity or blindness. Faith means to accept with open eyes and loving hearts the life that lies before us, knowing we will be taken care of and we will get what we need. Some say that faith *is* our relationship with God. It takes faith to let go and let God. Once we get rid of old habits, desires, and attachments, we may feel a need to attach to something else. Step Eleven suggests we attach to our Higher Power and nurture our faith to do our Higher Power's will.

No one is perfect. But if our motivations are clear, unselfish, and directed toward our Higher Power, our Eleventh Step will lead us to deep and lasting serenity.

STEP TWELVE

**Having had a spiritual awakening
as the result of these Steps, we tried to carry
this message to nicotine users, and to practice
these principles in all our affairs.**

The theme of the Twelfth Step is our newly found way of life—the freedom, joy, and serenity we have discovered through the awakening of our spirit. The power of the Twelfth Step is that it provides a guide for living the rest of our lives. There are three components to this Step. The first is the "spiritual awakening." This refers, of course, to where we have been in the past and what has happened to us. The second and third parts—to "carry this message" and "practice these principles"—are the guides for living and for our future.

If we look back over the course of the previous Steps, it is clear that we are seeing a process of spiritual awakening. There has been slow growth and change. Recognizing the unmanageability, which our addiction to nicotine spread over our lives, and learning to admit powerlessness did not happen without effort. It took work.

Beginning to believe in the notion of a Higher Power and starting to "Let go and Let God" was not easy for many of us. We struggled, resisted, and fought. But gradually, we managed to peel off another layer of the onion, and we got through Steps Two and Three. We continued to evolve, grow, and become aware.

The process continued. Gradually, step by step, we fought our way out of our deep slumber. Through what surely was the greatest struggle of our lives, we awakened to an altered sense of ourselves and our lives.

For many, the change included an awareness of the significance that we are on this planet, we are alive, and there is joy and happiness to be had, today, here and now.

We awakened from that time of slow suicide by nicotine use, when our spirits were drowned in a vast ocean of self-loathing, smashed by endless waves of craving, fear, and failure. We managed to find a way to get up on top of the waves and ride them and have fun, instead of letting them crash over us and pound us into the sand. We found a surfboard. We found a Higher Power. We found strength to save us from ourselves. We managed gradually to tap an inner resource of our own belief system, our own imagination, and our own faith—a God as we understood God. That God was someone, something, anyone, anything greater than we were.

We began to understand that the dis-ease we felt as nicotine addicts—the destructive self-consciousness, the inadequacies, the depression, the false bravado, the irrational aggressiveness, and the grim self-loathing—all grew out of a core sense of loneliness and fear. We thought we could do it by ourselves. We were alone and tried to ease the pain through nicotine.

Eventually, we were able to recognize the insanity caused by our self-imposed isolation. And then we allowed ourselves to find a companion we called a Higher Power.

We learned to work at keeping in contact with our soul, with our Higher Power. We found an ability to remain serene despite the ups and downs. We discovered that we could ride the waves.

With that discovery, life became and remains a series of small miracles and increments of wonder. We became less likely to wallow in self-pity or to brood an afternoon of our life away if we acknowledged, accepted, and welcomed our own spiritual existence. By finding the peace to ride on our planet's journey, every moment has its own reward. Every moment becomes sacred and enriches us because we learn to live today, here and now. Every raindrop that falls, every breath we breathe, every mountain we climb, and every wind which howls are all equally significant because we experience them. They exist, and when we exist as part of them, we are not alone. When we are not alone, we need not kill ourselves with nicotine.

This is what we mean when we talk about a spiritual awakening. This is what has happened through the process of the Steps.

Nonetheless, we remain addicts. And when we begin to experience the joys of being free from using nicotine, we run the risk of thinking once again that we can control things. That is the risk of being an addict. As the suffering of our nicotine past recedes, the temptations that got us in trouble return. This brings us to the latter parts of the Twelfth Step—the action plan for continuing to live free from nicotine.

We have learned the best way to keep our madness from resuming control of our lives is by sharing our new gift of life with those who are still suffering. We call it "carrying the message." We do this in two ways; we give away the gift we have received through sharing, and we let our lives be examples for others.

The way we carry the message to those who are still using nicotine is by sharing our experience, strength, and hope with them. It is simple and it is safe. We know of the miracle in our own lives, and we can share it with persons still suffering. Nevertheless, in sharing we need to be vigilant, remembering what we share is *our* experience—and no one else's.

We share our strength through honesty and humbleness. Moreover, we share the joy we have found through tapping into a new source for positive energy and the happiness we find in surrendering to something greater than ourselves—to a Higher Power.

As we share the gift of our own miracles, each act done in gratitude, no matter how small the separate undertaking may seem, has its own lessons and rewards for us. We give away what we have received and thereby get even more. We, who have been at the depths of despair and agony, learn as we help to lift others from that dreadful place. Our own joy increases as we see others being helped by what we have learned for ourselves. There is joy for us in helping a newcomer through just one craving for nicotine, since, as we know all so well, every single craving can be deadly.

What we actually do to help the nicotine user through a craving may be very simple and may not entail more than talking for a couple of minutes, or giving a hug or a squeeze on the hand. We know the pain because we have experienced it. Our joy in helping is not diminished by the simplicity of the undertaking because we understand its importance.

Through helping others, we learn compassion, patience, and tolerance. These wondrous gifts help us accept ourselves and reaffirm our own worth and growth. Our own simple, honest message of our recovery from nicotine addiction is powerful beyond belief. By attending meetings and making ourselves visible and available, we provide the greatest service possible. The more we participate and the more we are active, the better we can and do carry the message. We are not out to seek converts.

We show the way by example. This is the third part of Step Twelve. We practice the principles of recovery—the principles we have learned through the process of the Twelve Steps—and we practice them in all of our affairs. These principles include acceptance, surrender, humbleness, tolerance, patience, willingness, openness, love, hope, faith, trust, and joy.

These are the principles that rescued us from the loneliness and fear. They become ongoing principles of enjoying freedom, joy, and serenity in our everyday lives.

In addition, when we practice these principles in all our affairs, we do a superb job of carrying the message. Others who knew us before cannot help but notice the changes in us as we move forward in recovery. We carry the message by being in our own recovery all the time.

What started as a desperate focus on quitting the use of nicotine now blossoms and grows into a freedom to live. With awe and humility, we learn to enjoy the most precious gifts of all—the acceptance of our own humanness and the awareness that we are not alone.

Like life itself, the Steps are a process and a cycle. We live the Steps by practicing their positive principles in all our affairs. Step Twelve is not the end. It is the rest of life. It is freedom, joy and serenity.

Welcome To Nicotine Anonymous

Part IV

Twelve Traditions
of Nicotine Anonymous

1. Our common welfare should come first; personal recovery depends on Nicotine Anonymous unity.

2. For our group purpose, there is but one ultimate authority - a loving God as He may express Himself in our group conscience. Our leaders are but trusted servants; they do not govern.

3. The only requirement for Nicotine Anonymous membership is a desire to stop using nicotine.

4. Each group should be autonomous except in matters affecting other groups or Nicotine Anonymous as a whole.

5. Each group has but one primary purpose—to carry its message to the nicotine addict who still suffers.

6. A Nicotine Anonymous group ought never endorse, finance, or lend the Nicotine Anonymous name to any related facility or outside enterprise, lest problems of money, property, or prestige divert us from our primary purpose.

7. Every Nicotine Anonymous group ought to be fully self-supporting, declining outside contributions.

8. Nicotine Anonymous should remain forever nonprofessional, but our service centers may employ special workers.

9. Nicotine Anonymous, as such, ought never be organized; but we may create service boards or committees directly responsible to those they serve.

10. Nicotine Anonymous has no opinion on outside issues; hence, the Nicotine Anonymous name ought never be drawn into public controversy.

11. Our public relations policy is based on attraction rather than promotion. We need always maintain personal anonymity at the level of press, radio, TV, and films.

12. Anonymity is the spiritual foundation of all our Traditions, ever reminding us to place principles before personalities.

The Twelve Traditions reprinted and adapted with permission of Alcoholics Anonymous World Services Inc. Permission to reprint and adapt the Twelve Traditions does not mean that AA is affiliated with this program. AA is a program of recovery from alcoholism—use of the Twelve Steps in connection with programs and activities which are patterned after AA, but which address other problems does not imply otherwise.

The Twelve Traditions of Alcoholics Anonymous

1. Our common welfare should come first; personal recovery depends on Alcoholics Anonymous unity.

2. For our group purpose, there is but one ultimate authority -a loving God as He may express Himself in our group conscience. Our leaders are but trusted servants; they do not govern.

3. The only requirement for Alcoholics Anonymous membership is a desire to stop using alcohol.

4. Each group should be autonomous except in matters affecting other groups or Alcoholics Anonymous as a whole.

5. Each group has but one primary purpose—to carry its message to the alcoholic who still suffers.

6. An Alcoholics Anonymous group ought never endorse, finance, or lend the Alcoholics Anonymous name to any related facility or outside enterprise, lest problems of money, property, or prestige divert us from our primary purpose.

7. Every Alcoholics Anonymous group ought to be fully self-supporting, declining outside contributions.

8. Alcoholics Anonymous should remain forever nonprofessional, but our service centers may employ special workers.

9. Alcoholics Anonymous, as such, ought never be organized; but we may create service boards or committees directly responsible to those they serve.

10. Alcoholics Anonymous has no opinion on outside issues; hence, the Alcoholics Anonymous name ought never be drawn

into public controversy.

11. Our public relations policy is based on attraction rather than promotion. We need always maintain personal anonymity at the level of press, radio, and films.

12. Anonymity is the spiritual foundation of all our Traditions, ever reminding us to place principles before personalities.

The Twelve Traditions*

*Whenever a society or civilization perishes, there is always
one condition present; they forgot where they came from.*
—**Carl Sandburg**

Introduction

The Twelve Steps, based on ancient and universal spiritual
principles, describe a personal path for our recovery. The power
of individual recovery is in one member carrying the message to
the next, without any thought of personal gain or financial
reward—and it works.

The Twelve Traditions are to recovery fellowships what the
Twelve Steps are to the individual. They have spiritual
significance separately and as an equal partner to the Steps.
Groups are encouraged to give adequate time to discuss the
Traditions; while sponsors can emphasize this wisdom to
newcomers. If the Traditions are watered down, diluted, or
abandoned, a group's survival or an individual's recovery may be
placed at risk.

Bill Wilson (co-founder of Alcoholics Anonymous) first
drafted the Traditions as a distillation of the shared experiences
of the early Alcoholics Anonymous (AA) groups. They are the
result of trial and error, sometimes serious error. He expanded
them into their present form and they were adopted in 1950 at
the AA International Convention held in Cleveland.

The Traditions have withstood the test of time. They provide
a tried-and-true guide for groups while still allowing for
individuality. As Wilson poignantly notes in AA's first Tradition,
"On anvils of experience, the structure of our Society was
hammered out."

The Traditions were developed over time in response to
problems as they arose. They are based on experience particular
to the common welfare of Alcoholics Anonymous. Our
fellowship has adopted them because they have served AA well.

Our fellowship is non-commercial and non-professional, our
leaders but trusted servants. No member can tell another, "You
can't do that," or "You must do this." If a group fails to observe

the Traditions, it risks the possibility of confusion and conflict. Confusion and conflict may turn newcomers away, depriving them of the benefits Nicotine Anonymous has to offer.

The Traditions provide form and unity to our entire fellowship. They help guide local groups in a way that has worked at bringing recovery to many people over many years. They gently keep the focus on our primary purpose and ensure that any member of our fellowship can go to any meeting and find the same basic spiritual principles at work. They foster a safe place for each individual by stressing the importance of group unity. Humility is the foundation on which the Traditions are built. The Traditions protect our fellowship from our individual shortcomings; they protect us from ourselves and keep us right-sized, just like the Steps.

May we all continue to deepen our understanding of these principles so that our recovery and our fellowship continue to grow and serve all those who seek freedom from nicotine.

TRADITION ONE

Our common welfare should come first; personal recovery depends on Nicotine Anonymous unity.

Does this mean that the individual must conform to all aspects of our program? Certainly not! The sentence in AA's "Big Book" that introduces the Steps reads- "Here are the steps we took, which are *suggested* (italics our emphasis) as a program of recovery." Similarly, the Traditions use the word "ought" and "should" as *guidelines,* offered from experience.

Tradition One reminds us that our common welfare comes first. By putting our common welfare first, individuals put themselves second. Each individual member of Nicotine Anonymous is a part of the whole. Nicotine Anonymous needs to live as an entity so that we, as individual members, may continue to live—free of nicotine. We come to understand that each of us needs to internalize the principles of recovery because our lives depend on our adherence to spiritual principles. Individually, we are "one for all"; as a group we are "all for one." As a fellowship we remain united on core issues of recovery. If not, we jeopardize personal recovery and risk weakening the bonds of our fellowship.

One of our core issues was addressed by group conscience at the 1988 World Services Conference which established a clear understanding for our definition of *abstinence*. Since 1988, we define abstinence as "a state that begins when all use of nicotine ceases." Although our name was *Smokers Anonymous* at the time, we collectively agreed that abstinence from nicotine was our primary purpose, not any particular method of delivery. In 1990, our name became Nicotine Anonymous, which broadened our awareness and outreach as a program to include nicotine addiction in *all* forms.

In accordance with Tradition Ten, we have "no opinion on outside issues" such as any product used for a withdrawal aid. Each individual determines his or her nicotine free date. The fellowship as a whole and by extension, each group provides a structure and a unity of purpose which allows us to welcome all, without judgment. The group's sole objective is recovery for the individual. Individual and group survival depends on friendly relationships between group members. In our meetings, members share their personal experiences about recovery while other members listen. While each member has a right to express his or her views, an individual member may have to accept the group's majority voice graciously. An open mind is helpful when listening to other members' ideas or opinions.

Spiritually healthy groups usually have members who feel some "ownership" of their "home" group through active participation. They willingly volunteer to take on the responsibilities of running the group. They serve as chairperson, secretary, or treasurer. They take a literature or meeting setup commitment. Generally, these members have benefited from our program of recovery and share that experience in a service role clearly visible to the newcomer.

On the other hand, what happens when an individual member refuses to accept a group decision? Each member has to decide for himself or herself how to respond to such a situation. Some may feel the issue is important enough to leave the group, others may decide to simply agree to disagree. A majority vote does not necessarily mean it is "right." Anyone has the option to start a new meeting. It can also occur that a member remains in the group, but becomes resentful, and this may have a negative influence on the group. If other group members become uncomfortable or are scared away, the group may eventually fold. What to do?

No member of Nicotine Anonymous has authority over another. But the group, speaking out of a group conscience does have authority. However, this is an essential reason for members to study the wisdom in all the Traditions in order that they may

*The Twelve Traditions reprinted and adapted with permission of Alcoholics Anonymous World Service, Inc. Permission to reprint and adapt the Twelve Traditions does not mean that AA is affiliated with this program. AA is a program of recovery from alcoholism— use of the Twelve Traditions in connection with programs and activities which are patterned after AA, but which address other problems, does not imply otherwise.

better fulfill the group's primary purpose (Tradition Five). Being guided by this unified wisdom, the group has a better opportunity to know what the common welfare is and to put it first. Then, by speaking with one voice, this strengthens the unity of Nicotine Anonymous. If we adhere to our name, Nicotine Anonymous, then we can Keep it Simple and make it easier for the newcomer to understand and practice our program of recovery.

TRADITION TWO

For our group purpose there is but one ultimate authority—a loving God as He may express Himself in our group conscience. Our leaders are but trusted servants; they do not govern.

We frequently say that Nicotine Anonymous is a "We" program. Clearly, many nicotine addicts who believed themselves hopeless have found recovery through the fellowship of Nicotine Anonymous. Although they admitted they were powerless over nicotine on their own, they somehow came to experience miraculous relief from the obsession to use nicotine through the power of a loving God (as they understood that power) acting through the group.

Reinforcing the idea that Nicotine Anonymous is a "We" program, Tradition Two reminds us that final authority in matters affecting Nicotine Anonymous groups never resides with any one individual, but with the group itself through its group conscience. What, exactly, does the term "group conscience" mean?

At the most basic level, it means an issue that requires action is brought to a Nicotine Anonymous group for discussion. The course of action to be taken is then determined by a vote of the group's members. The use of the word "conscience," implies that there is a moral imperative to group votes. In fact, there is.

Underlying all the other Traditions, Tradition Five says, "Each group has but one primary purpose—to carry its message to the nicotine addict who still suffers." Each member, then, when participating in a group conscience, should consider whether or not their vote helps the group fulfill its primary purpose. This means members put personal preferences aside and vote with this higher purpose in mind. When this happens—when members put aside their own agendas and act for the common good we believe a loving Higher Power's will is truly made evident through our group conscience.

Since we acknowledge that a Higher Power expresses itself through our group conscience, does that mean that decisions made by a group should never be changed? No, this is not

117

necessarily the case. For example, when our fellowship was first formed, the earliest members decided we should be known as "Smokers Anonymous." At the time, the name was entirely appropriate because the early members were all smokers. Years later, however, it became clear that our Higher Power no longer desired us to be known as "Smokers Anonymous." This became evident when it was brought to our attention that the name, "Smokers Anonymous" was already legally registered by a doctor who operated a program that had nothing to do with a Twelve Step process of recovery.

This presented a real problem to our fledgling organization. The doctor was willing to license the name to us for a substantial annual licensing fee. The fellowship could not afford to pay such a fee. The dilemma was brought to the Fifth Annual Smokers Anonymous World Services Conference, held in Phoenix, Arizona, in 1990. According to the Bylaws of our fellowship, the annual World Services Conference serves as "the collective conscience of the fellowship of Nicotine Anonymous [then Smokers Anonymous] as a whole."

A member present at this pivotal debate in our fellowship's history described the process as "the most dramatic evidence of the guiding hand of our collective Higher Power at work that I have ever seen." That discussion had started from a nearly unanimous collective position to "fight the good fight" to keep the full name "Smokers Anonymous." The idea was that any program called "Anonymous," as applied to recovery from addiction, should be reserved for the exclusive use of bona fide 12-step programs.

Within a couple of hours, the nearly unanimous collective position had shifted 180 degrees from a combative determination to keep the term "Smokers" to the acceptance of the term "Nicotine." It was something like "of course we are inclusive and our recovery process is about gaining and maintaining freedom from a drug, not a delivery system." That member described the awesome shift, under the guidance of a loving collective Higher Power "like the tide coming in." The rising tide inevitably swept participants in the discussion to the conclusion that it was time to accept the natural evolution of our fellowship into the more inclusive Nicotine Anonymous.

Changing the name of our fellowship is an example of group conscience operating at the fellowship-wide level. However, group conscience occurs at several different levels throughout Nicotine Anonymous. Group conscience is also expressed at weekly Nicotine Anonymous meetings, at monthly intergroup meetings, and at periodic meetings of the officers of the World Service Office (WSO) of Nicotine Anonymous. There are also many occasions when special committees are formed for conference or retreat planning, revising the Bylaws of Nicotine Anonymous, proposing new or revised literature, and so on. Although these committees may have a chairperson coordinating the efforts of the committee, they use group conscience to reach accord within the committee.

At the group level, members utilize group conscience to determine a wide variety of items. For example, groups need officers—members who are willing to serve in positions such as secretary, chairperson, or treasurer. Many groups hold periodic business meetings for the purpose of electing officers and determining other business items. These include how long officers will serve, how long members are required to be abstinent to be eligible for office, whether or not the group will serve coffee at meetings, and how much the group can afford to donate to their local intergroup and to Nicotine Anonymous World Services. There are many other group related items that are decided by group conscience.

TRADITION THREE

The only requirement for Nicotine Anonymous membership is a desire to stop using nicotine.

As a worldwide fellowship, Nicotine Anonymous wants to reach out and include any nicotine user who seeks to join us in the pursuit of living free from nicotine. This one requirement for membership keeps it simple, and keeps it sane. We have one point to rally around, to establish our equality, and simply welcome all newcomers.

We have been freely given the precious gift of recovery and have had the deadly grip of nicotine addiction lifted from our lives. All that was asked of us was that we have a desire (no matter how small) to stop using nicotine. Therefore, how could we now presume to deny this gift to newcomers?

Any differences in beliefs should not interfere with a newcomer's access to the program or our support. Certainly it is true that there are those among us who discovered for themselves that it was necessary for them to shed old beliefs in order to find a new peace in recovery. Becoming a Nicotine Anonymous member, just as forming one's own belief system, is a personal decision. In this way, Tradition Three also protects us from getting caught up in making injurious judgments of others, especially of those of us still (or relapsed) in the powerful grip of nicotine.

As a spiritual program, acknowledging the desire to stop using nicotine embraces the spirit within and avoids judgments toward the behavior of the disease. Therefore, it is *not* necessary for newcomers to have already stopped using nicotine before they join us. Some newcomers may find it difficult to recognize or acknowledge that desire. For some of us, the desire was so small, we did not even feel we had a desire until day after day, week after week, meeting after meeting, we finally recognized it and eventually got free.

By having only this ONE requirement for membership, we also maintain our openness to all who seek recovery. Newcomers don't have to belong to any other group, believe in God, donate money, or work the Steps in a certain way to join. We are not afraid of the emotions expressed when one stops using nicotine.

No one is required to be rational or lucid or say all the correct things at meetings. We've been there. We do not exclude anyone from our program for any reason including race, reputation, creed, sexual orientation, gender, disability, or place of origin. If newcomers are not sure the desire to stop using nicotine is within them, but they are willing to find out, they are welcome here.

Most of us lived in a dark pit of denial, alienation, and pain caused by nicotine addiction for many years. We would not leave a suffering addict at the bottom of that pit alone—not when we have the rope of recovery that we can toss down to them. Granted, they have to be willing to take hold of the rope in order to climb out and join us. But, that is all we require.

Some of our members feel they were actually pulled up out of their addiction by the simple act of asking for help. Others find that the gift of recovery from nicotine was more difficult to accept, having to struggle up that rope and slip back down many times before maintaining their abstinence from nicotine. Tradition Three keeps our doors open and our hearts reaching out. Our shared stories reveal both the worst aspects of being caught inside this addiction and the joys of coming out to a new freedom. We are not only aware of the dangers of nicotine addiction, but also very grateful for the spiritual gift of recovery that makes our freedom possible. Therefore, we keep showing up at meetings and tossing down the rope of our truth, which is our experience, strength, and hope, so that others may be lifted to freedom.

Although this program provides us with a spiritual approach to fulfill the desire for freedom, joy, and peace, most nicotine addicts fell into the pit as immature teenagers. We were often driven by a similar desire to feel more freedoms and joys, and then spent many years chasing after them by using nicotine. Coming to see this desire anew is often challenging. At first, we may not have wanted to give up our drug. Perhaps we feared that we could not live without it. Despite attending many meetings or possibly abstaining from nicotine use for periods of time, we felt sure that we had no honest desire to stop.

However, once we discussed this issue with other members, we found others who had not initially felt a tremendous desire to stop either. Some had even repeated in meetings that they did not want to put down nicotine at all. Some of us only wanted to live and were afraid we would die if we continued to use nicotine.

Some of us only had a desire to find our Higher Power's will for us. Some of us wanted to improve our health. Many of us only wanted to want to stop using nicotine. We have come to understand that any of these, or even the simple willingness to show up at meetings, can be defined as a desire to stop using nicotine.

Also, there have been those who had difficulty with the issue of nicotine. While they felt they had a desire to quit smoking or chewing tobacco, they may not have felt ready to give up some other nicotine delivery systems. Each of us decides on a way to begin our own process and that a desire to stop using nicotine in all forms may follow in time.

Once clear of the smoke screen nicotine placed between our true desires and thoughts, our collective experience has shown that we do indeed have a great desire to stay free of this cunning and dangerous drug. In addition, most of us also have a great desire to really live our lives. For many of us, going back to using nicotine would mean giving up wonderful new joys that have been added to our lives. Things such as hiking, aerobics, singing, sharing time with friends, intimacy in our relationships, our new found health, and even the ability to sit still through a movie or a plane ride would be taken from us if we returned to our addiction. Our desire to continue with our new lives now far outweighs any desire we may still have for our drug.

So, if you wish to become a Nicotine Anonymous member, come join us. If you are willing to call us or walk into our rooms, we have faith that the desire to stop is within you. No matter who you are, no matter how many other addictions you may have, no matter what your troubles are, you will find some among us have them too. We want you here with us. We are keeping you in our thoughts and hope you will choose to join us in the wonderful life and freedom we have found after we got free of nicotine. Tradition Three is our welcome to Nicotine Anonymous!

TRADITION FOUR

Each group should be autonomous except in matters affecting other groups or Nicotine Anonymous as a whole.

According to the history of our fellowship, Nicotine Anonymous groups (once known as Smokers Anonymous) existed autonomously without even knowing of each other's existence. They each were able to help addicts achieve freedom from nicotine. They practiced the Twelve Steps and/or provided each other with fellowship.

In essence, a group is any two or more nicotine addicts gathered together to achieve abstinence and the group claims no other official association. While our intergroups and World Services office perform valuable functions, they only exist to support the groups and their members. The groups are the heart of Nicotine Anonymous. It is here that recovery and abstinence are attained, sponsors and sponsees are united, and miracles occur. These groups can and have conducted their own matters since before our fellowship officially came into existence.

This is why we can confidently allow our groups today to continue to make all their own decisions without interfering in their affairs. Each group is free to do such things as arrange their own meeting format, select topics of discussion and speakers, provide anniversary tokens to recognize abstinence, and determine whether and when to donate group funds to an intergroup or World Services. As between individual members, the relationship between groups and World Services is strengthened by trust, both given and honored.

We do encourage all groups to confer with other groups, their intergroup, and World Services whenever they embark on something which may affect other groups or the fellowship. Seeking guidance to gauge an impulse or idea is one of the principles that support our recovery process. A case occurred many years ago when the chairman of an intergroup was contacted by the maker of a new alternative nicotine product. The company offered to finance and staff a toll-free number for them if they would provide support for their customers and include their pamphlets on the groups' literature tables. After conferring with members of other groups, the offer was wisely declined. Besides damaging the reputation of any groups involved, such an endeavor would surely harm the entire fellowship.

Even with so many temptations to go astray, we still understand that groups need to make their own decisions and their own mistakes. We have the right to learn from our mistakes. As we see later in Tradition Nine, the fellowship has little but advisory authority over the groups in most matters. We can only pass on the experience of other groups in similar situations. Ultimately, we need to have faith in our Higher Power who has guided our groups through many tough choices such as the following:

Many of the New York City area groups evolved from old "A.A. for Non-Smokers" meetings. These were A.A. members who came together to address their addiction to nicotine. Some of these groups changed their name to Nicotine Anonymous, while others kept their old "A.A. for Non-Smokers" name. The New York Metropolitan Area Intergroup had a very brief meeting list and many were eager to list as many meetings as possible. It was voted that these groups could not be listed because of their outside affiliation. Since then, many of these have decided by group conscience to become Nicotine Anonymous meetings. This decision had to be made by the individual groups themselves.

Perhaps the freedom that we offer our groups is part of the attraction of our fellowship. It allows each group to create meetings that best serve its membership. While it is comforting to go to meetings around the world and see the same Twelve Steps and Twelve Traditions, the varied formats, readings, stories, and customs make for a wonderful variety. This serves to keep things interesting and to help us learn to approach our recovery with an open mind.

TRADITION FIVE

Each group has but one primary purpose—to carry its message to the nicotine addict who still suffers.

In itself, this Tradition carries a message to all group members. First, members of each group, acting as a unified whole, have *one primary purpose* to fulfill. Second, we have a valuable *message* that we are to share. Third, to whom we are to carry this message is specifically identifies—*the nicotine addict who still suffers*.

At a group level, we communicate our message both in the meaning of our words as well as the manner of our actions. Having a primary purpose serves us like a guiding star, letting us know when we are on course. With recovery comes a newfound enthusiasm which can lead members of a group to try to be many things to many people. A group need take care not to become diluted or distracted regarding its sense of purpose.

Our experience with nicotine and recovery is what we know best. Sharing our story does not require special talents or training. We can each offer what we know and have come to believe. Carrying the message is also accomplished without speaking, when we quietly listen to our fellow members. By focusing on our primary purpose, a group increases the likelihood of acting in good faith toward our principles and maintaining unity in the process. In this simplicity, there is strength.

As a fellowship, we understand this spiritual principle: in order to keep the recovery we have received we need to keep giving this *gift* away to others who still suffer. To ignore this truth, we risk a relapse as individuals and risk the preservation of the group. This is a mission of love spreading out to members either still in the grip of nicotine or struggling with other aspects of their recovery.

Although we are a program grounded in anonymity, we do not grow in the dark. This love is also expressed in our outreach efforts to those who have not yet heard about our program. Carrying the message is our recovery in action. We look to act in a manner that attracts others that they may be granted the same peace we seek. Our warm welcome opens our hearts and keeps us from the isolation of addiction. A newcomer's struggle helps remind us of where we have come from, ever deepening our gratitude for another day free from nicotine.

Nicotine Anonymous has five tools to help us live nicotine free. The five tools are: meetings, phone/email list, literature, sponsorship, and service. The tools are also a means by which we can carry our message to others who seek help. Meetings carry the message by reminding us to turn our attention toward the solution rather than the problem. In this, there is hope and strength. Sharing provides an opportunity for newcomers to identify with others' past experience as they hear and see possibilities for change. They witness honesty and hope in a safe and supportive setting. The firsthand message our members offer is unique and powerful.

A group's phone list grows whenever a member becomes willing to add his or her name and offer support between meetings. This list is especially important to the still suffering addict whose desire to get free may struggle to be heard above the nagging of nicotine.

Newcomers not yet comfortable speaking at meetings may find more ease using other such forms of communication. We have a gentle message that each may heed at his or her own pace.

Our literature is written by members, reviewed by trusted servants, and deemed official by delegates who vote at our annual Conferences to ensure that it carries our message. Our experience is available in several forms such as pamphlets, books, CDs, and MP3s.. World Services and some intergroups publish newsletters where members contribute their individual experience as well. We know that if we do not reach out to those still suffering we risk stagnating and having no vital purpose.

Sponsorship is the personal embodiment of the principle for how one keeps his or her recovery by kindly giving it away to a sponsee. Sponsors carry the message by sharing the journey of recovery on a one-to-one basis, by listening with care, and by demonstrating through action how Nicotine Anonymous works.

Service is our gratitude in action. Doing service carries our message of commitment and responsibility. Service can also carry our message as a means of making amends and showing we have improved our behavior or attitude. Members who serve become role models, often stretching beyond former fears and limitations in order to fulfill our primary purpose.

Having a primary purpose keeps the intent of our message simple and clear, which may lessen whatever suspicions those still suffering might have about a group. Many of us had doubts and fears about joining groups when we first arrived. For example, newcomers may have concerns about religious issues when they learn we are a spiritually based program. It is imperative that we honor Our Preamble regarding Nicotine Anonymous not being allied with any religious or political organization.

By appropriately carrying our message, each group shows the still suffering nicotine addict we care and what is possible when not under the influence of nicotine. A primary purpose provides us with a focus that reminds us to recognize and value priorities. All this and more reveals the full dimension of our recovery message.

TRADITION SIX

A Nicotine Anonymous group ought never endorse, finance, or lend the Nicotine Anonymous name to any related facility or outside enterprise, lest problems of money, property, and prestige divert us from our primary purpose.

At the turn of the 21st century, this Tradition was referenced in decisions made about linking our web page to web pages of other organizations. Some members felt that linking would imply affiliation. This Tradition allows us to *cooperate* with outside entities, but not to *affiliate*. To discern the difference between those two words (*cooperate* and *affiliate*) was a challenge for some Nicotine Anonymous members.

Some members wanted us to throw caution to the wind and link up to any and everything that had anything to do with nicotine cessation. Some felt it would "only be fair" because many organizations send us referrals. However, as of this writing, our group conscience has decided to have our web page make mention of other resources, but not provide links to those sites. We have also decided that other sites can have links to us, but we will not provide reciprocal links to them.

We see other organizations help people to quit smoking and some of their "graduates" come into our rooms. Some of our members have wondered why we shouldn't merge with them and take advantage of some of their infrastructure. Or, if that is out of order, they wonder why we can't at least endorse them, especially in cities and towns where we don't have any meetings. People are always asking for the names and phone numbers of rehabs where people can go for a week of nicotine abstinence. Some of our members have wondered if we should send them to the Nicotine Anonymous web page so they can click on a link to get the information they so desperately need. These members have asked, "Isn't that helping the still suffering addict?" Tradition Six tells us that this is not the way our program will help them. Tradition Six helps us to *keep it simple* and to have appropriate, yet useful relationships with other organizations on a fellowship-wide level.

Although each party starts as a separate entity when a relationship is established, there occurs (either in actuality or perception) an inevitable blending of identities and/or policies. The difficulty for us would exist if, for example, we were to form such a relationship with another organization. While both may have the common interest of good health and spirituality, the affiliation would have each organization losing some of its original character and specialty. Tradition Six protects us from diluting or altering what we are and what we do. Tradition Six maintains our fellowship's unique ability to help the nicotine addict who still suffers.

We recognize that people do have other problems and members should be able to inform other members about resources where they might seek additional assistance without the risk of our fellowship becoming affiliated with those other groups. For example, people often gain some weight when they quit smoking. On a personal basis, there is nothing wrong with sharing information about another fellowship or organization that could be of further help to a fellow member, but for our fellowship to officially affiliate with that other group or organization would be a major mistake.

During the 1980s, one of our members was contacted by a drug company which was producing a nicotine gum to help people quit smoking. The company was going to offer us a much needed toll free number along with a person who would maintain a database of our worldwide meeting list. This service would have been completely free to us. In exchange, we would have been required to put this company's literature on our literature table with our own conference-approved literature. It was a tempting deal, but thanks to the wisdom of Tradition Six we declined their offer.

We have a very powerful safety valve in the form of Tradition Six. Helping the still suffering addict is our primary purpose. Tradition Six helps our fellowship focus our efforts on that essential task and avoid becoming diverted or diluted by an outside enterprise or even a related facility.

TRADITION SEVEN

Every Nicotine Anonymous group ought to be fully self-supporting, declining outside contributions.

One clear function of this Tradition is to guide how we accept monetary contributions only from our members and not from any outside contributors, no matter how well-meaning those offers may be. This way each group maintains its autonomy and our fellowship remains independent. It is vital that we do not accept any outside contributions, lest we become dependent on that outside individual or group for our survival. Our survival needs to be determined by our own contributions; otherwise we may become involved in outside issues and politics. These other agendas could weaken and confuse our message, threatening or even ending our mission.

Early in the life of a particular Nicotine Anonymous group, the group was very graciously offered a meeting place free of charge. Several members argued that being a small group, survival depended on accepting that offer. However, through a group conscience, it was determined that in order for the group to maintain its autonomy, it would have to decline this very generous offer. Instead, they decided to negotiate a monthly "donation" in return for a meeting room. The group realized this was a vital decision that protected the integrity of our message and honored this Tradition of our fellowship. Even if it meant this one meeting might close without outside contributions, the group was willing to accept that possibility.

Looking more deeply into this Tradition, we cannot be totally self-supporting without each of us contributing service to our group, intergroup, and World Services. Service is not only one of the tools of personal recovery, it is the life blood for our entire fellowship. If we only *take* from the fellowship, we no longer *make* a fellowship. Whenever any one of us is content to sit back and let "someone else" make the necessary commitments, the existence of a group, and eventually Nicotine Anonymous itself is threatened.

Self supporting through service means actions such as attending both group and business meetings on a regular basis, sharing at meetings, working the Steps, sponsoring people, setting up and cleaning up meetings, subscribing and contributing to fellowship newsletters, as well as taking on chairperson, treasurer, or secretary positions. Self-supporting service, as much or more than monetary contributions, will insure our continued ability to serve all nicotine users who seek our help. Thus, by honoring this Tradition, we maintain our primary purpose and the spiritual foundation upon which our fellowship is based.

TRADITION EIGHT

Nicotine Anonymous should remain forever non-professional, but our service centers may employ special workers.

In order to maintain our spiritual foundation we need to determine appropriate boundaries regarding involvement with professionals. The manner in which members serve our fellowship needs to be in accordance with all our Traditions and Steps. The integrity of our program's principles should not become compromised or brought under suspicion with matters related to monetary profits.

A function of our primary principle, anonymity, is that it affords all members an equality of status. If some members were to carry our message of recovery identified as "paid Nicotine Anonymous professionals" an inequality of status would result. Such implied inequality could lead other members to feel less valued or less inclined to serve the group or even share their story. A member who gains financially for carrying the message of Nicotine Anonymous would not be in keeping with the spiritual principle of personal recovery—to freely give what we have been freely given.

Our Preamble states that there are no dues or fees for Nicotine Anonymous membership. Tradition Three establishes the only requirement for membership is a desire to stop using nicotine. Having members charge money as professionals for doing Step Twelve work would be contrary to our principles.

However, Tradition Seven guides our groups to be self-supporting. In order for our fellowship to function effectively and efficiently there are practical and appropriate circumstances for members, who understand our program, to be paid or have expenses covered for services rendered. These members would be considered "special workers." They help with the regular tasks of operating the fellowship in a way that supports our efforts to help nicotine addicts.

For example, it could be appropriate to compensate a professional office manager with the necessary skills to address the ongoing business of an intergroup or World Services. Fellowship funds could pay a member whose job it is to respond to literature orders and mail packages to groups and individual members. Although volunteers offer their talents freely to serve in many capacities, they cannot be expected to carry the message of recovery as well as carry the full load of running every aspect our fellowship.

Additionally, health care professionals can arrange to have meetings available at their agencies to serve clients and patients. A member may open a nicotine rehab facility as a career. As long as compensation is not received for directly doing Nicotine Anonymous Twelfth Step work as a Nicotine Anonymous member, they are not violating this Tradition. Therapists who are also Nicotine Anonymous members can treat clients for nicotine addiction, but when attending Nicotine Anonymous meetings simply as a member they have no more authority or status than any other member. Meetings are not a "place of business" and no professional should solicit clients at meetings. No member can be a "Nicotine Anonymous professional."

Nicotine Anonymous meetings are not professionally facilitated therapy groups. Therefore, we would not endorse any one form of therapy because Tradition Ten guides us away from claiming an opinion on outside issues. Our program is unique. It consists of the Twelve Steps and Twelve Traditions. These, together with the five tools, are what we know and what we offer.

TRADITION NINE

Nicotine Anonymous as such ought never be organized; but we may create service boards or committees directly responsible to those they serve.

At first, this statement may pose a paradox about our program. If we have no organization, then how is it that we have our intergroups, World Service office, board, and committees? Are these not examples of organization? Without organization, will we not have anarchy?

Well, yes, we do have anarchy. Anarchy is the absence of government, and we certainly have no government. However, what we do have are servants, staff, and volunteers who serve the entirety of our fellowship. Whether we speak of a telephone volunteer, an officer of the board, or paid office assistant, each works to serve the needs of the fellowship in general and individual members upon request.

There is actually great comfort to be derived from this lack of structure. The leaders of each group, committee, or board are there to serve the members, not to dictate or impose their will. No one can tell any member or group what they must do. Like the Steps, our guidelines and Traditions are suggestions. In the experience of many of our members, not working the Steps has had extreme consequences, often leading to relapse. The same is true of our Traditions. We have often seen non-adherence to the Traditions lead to a group's demise. Even so, we can only make suggestions based on our experiences of how other groups dealt with similar situations. There is no enforcement or judicial branch of our fellowship. In fact, it is the servants and leaders who have to answer to the members and groups of Nicotine Anonymous.

Groups, intergroups, and World Services each set their own parameters for choosing its servants and leaders. There may be a simple rotation of commitments or a formal election of officers. Those elected or chosen derive their authority solely from those who have selected them. They are charged with the task of serving the fellowship in line with the principles of the program and to uphold the Twelve Traditions of Nicotine Anonymous.

In the early days, groups existed without regional intergroups or a World Services office. Today, these regional committees and World Services provide essential services such as printing meeting lists, distributing literature, answering phones and correspondence, and spreading the message of our fellowship wherever possible. World Services prints all Conference-approved literature. Over the years these services have proved essential to our fellowship's existence and our personal recovery. Most of us could not imagine the program without them.

When our volunteers truly embrace the humble principles of service, fellowship, and selflessness, there is no need to grab vainly for the powers of control, prestige, and selfishness. A spirit of cooperation and a singleness of purpose are all that is necessary to provide Nicotine Anonymous with its unique structure of service, fellowship, and recovery.

TRADITION TEN

Nicotine Anonymous has no opinion on outside issues hence the Nicotine Anonymous name ought never be drawn into public controversy.

Tradition Ten helps remind us to fulfill our primary purpose, which is to carry the message to the nicotine addict that still suffers. Therefore, Nicotine Anonymous should not divert its attention by involving itself in outside issues or public controversy.

As recovering nicotine addicts we know that the use of nicotine is harmful and some may, in fact, believe that it should be banned, controlled, or limited. Therefore, it is tempting to say that we should support lawsuits against tobacco companies, take out ads that support outlawing nicotine, participate with groups that want to ban smoking, or support politicians who seek to limit places where people can smoke.

Tradition 10 clearly tells us "No." We have no opinion as a group about tobacco companies, various nicotine products, or the nicotine use of others. True, we as individual addicts may have differing opinions on these subjects. However, as a group, as Nicotine Anonymous, we state or take no position.

Smoking, dipping, chewing—these are things that we all enjoyed at one point while using nicotine. How we stopped using, how we came to believe, how we gained freedom from this powerful addiction—these are the things we share in order to help the person who is still suffering.

No member, using the name of Nicotine Anonymous *OR* claiming to be a spokesperson for our program *OR* as a representative of Nicotine Anonymous, should ever express an opinion, at the public level, on outside controversial issues, particularly those of politics, nicotine reform, or religion. Nicotine Anonymous neither endorses nor opposes any cause or candidate. We do not even oppose the manufacture, sale, or use of nicotine products. As a fellowship, we have no opinion on government subsidies to tobacco farmers or when, how, and where nicotine is packaged or consumed. Although Nicotine

Anonymous is a spiritual program, we have no opinion on religion or religious institutions. Many of us come from various religious and political backgrounds. To insist that any member support a particular religion or political cause would not only destroy our fellowship, but would violate the first Tradition regarding the primary importance of our common unity.

The founders of the Alcoholics Anonymous program wisely decided not to take on the alcohol manufacturers or participate in a temperance movement to ban alcohol. They realized that such a move would be futile and would likely destroy the foundation of their recovery. Similarly, Nicotine Anonymous cannot divert from our primary purpose in order to rail against the tobacco companies or promote legislation as to how and when people may smoke, dip, or chew.

Also, many nicotine users chose to end their use of nicotine with the help of nicotine withdrawal aids such as the nicotine patch, nicotine gum, or prescription medications. Use of such substances is up to each individual and should not be dictated or criticized by the group. Providing support in order to live free of nicotine is our primary purpose, not how an individual member may choose to get free.

This Tradition may be personally difficult to live up to because we probably all have opinions on such issues. However, when we act as a representative of Nicotine Anonymous, we need to avoid public debates on such controversial issues, focusing instead on maintaining the sanity and strength of our fellowship so that we can be helpful to the nicotine addict who still suffers.

TRADITION ELEVEN

Our public relations policy is based on attraction rather than promotion; we need always maintain personal anonymity at the level of press, radio, television, and films.

As nicotine addicts our lives were out of control and unmanageable. We used nicotine to the extreme. One was not enough; thousands were not enough. We saw no problem in the extremes we went to in order to get and maintain a daily supply of nicotine. Our behavior with nicotine, whether inhaling it or chewing it, lacked boundaries as our smoke, butts, or spit polluted the environs wherever we went.

Like many of the principles of our program, Tradition Eleven guides us in our recovery to have appropriate limits when we "carry the message" to those outside of our fellowship. The integrity and longevity of our fellowship depends on this time-tested principle. Certainly we want people to know about what we offer. However, it is essential that the focus remain on the program rather than the personalities within the fellowship. We want people *attracted* to our program because of its principles, not because of who is in it. Anonymity not only protects the individual, it protects the program from the human shortcomings we all have.

Anonymity is not a matter for each member to determine for himself or herself. If a member was to think: "I don't care if the public knows I am a Nicotine Anonymous member, I have nothing to hide" this would be overlooking that this is a "WE" program, not a "ME" program. Nicotine Anonymous' spiritual principles include humility, which is essential to our recovery. Consider if one member grabs the spotlight, then others may become jealous or try to compete. This would erode unity. Additionally, Nicotine Anonymous members ought to remain mindful that, although we are not affiliated with Alcoholics Anonymous (and other 12- step fellowships), we are part of a recovery community sharing this program and we need to show our respect and gratitude by honoring this Tradition for the sake of all.

The media is filled with advertisements using celebrities to make personal endorsements of products. The ads may be effective for those corporations, but there are risks. If that personality "falls from grace" or one's "pedestal" becomes a target for the press, the situation could reflect poorly on the company or product. Nicotine Anonymous acknowledges relapses are a reality from which no member is immune. Nicotine Anonymous accepts the wisdom learned by Alcoholics Anonymous- promotions highlighting *the person* are not the best way for us to carry the message.

Many newcomers hear about us by word of mouth from other members or by local meeting notices inviting anyone with a desire to stop using nicotine to come to a meeting. Publicity in various forms has also been an important way for the nicotine addict who still suffers to hear about Nicotine Anonymous. Early in our organization's history, a member wrote a *Reader's Digest* story about our program and the article significantly raised public awareness of our existence. Also, columns in *Dear Abby* and *Ann Landers* referring to our fellowship caught many an eye. These were not examples of self-promotion because they kept the focus on the fellowship.

There are many ways to appropriately publicize what we offer. NAWS has pamphlets suitable for outreach efforts such as "Introducing Nicotine Anonymous," "To the Newcomer and Sponsorship in Nicotine Anonymous," and "Introducing Nicotine Anonymous to the Medical Profession." Nicotine Anonymous World Services also has CDs with a public service announcement that members can ask local radio stations to broadcast. Some other examples are as follows: local meeting announcements placed in newspapers and on palm cards; information provided to local chapters of national health organizations; Nicotine Anonymous literature presented at health fairs or offered to the offices of health professionals and hospitals.

If a member were to write a book or be interviewed by public media there are some appropriate options. Individuals can use their full name if they forgo mentioning they are Nicotine Anonymous members and simply identify themselves as nicotine addicts. If individuals are identifying themselves as Nicotine Anonymous members, the other option would be to conceal their faces and use first names only.

In public settings *without* public media present such as a health fair or facility, members can use first names only when presenting Nicotine Anonymous materials and/or sharing their experience, strength, and hope. In addition, whenever a member identifies him or herself as a member whether or not in a public media situation, he or she is advised to explain that he or she speaks only of his or her own experience and opinion, and as such does not necessarily represent the organization as a whole.

Many of our members did not show up to a meeting the first time they heard about it or work the Steps the first time they read them. They could not be "sold" this program, they had to become ready. The best way we carry this message is by our sharing our experience, strength, and hope at meetings, serving in outreach efforts, by frankly explaining what Nicotine Anonymous is about, and by living the results of our spiritual awakening by practicing program principles in our daily lives. If what nicotine addicts see and hear *attracts* them, they will find our warm welcome.

Out of respect for others, we do not tell people that they *need our program* or what they *should* do. We do not ensure everyone a "guarantee of success." We are not selling, we are showing.

Faith and humility are spiritual principles, and to remain a spiritual program, we need to practice faith and humility in our public relations policy.

TRADITION TWELVE

Anonymity is the spiritual foundation of all our Traditions, ever reminding us to place principles before personalities.

Anonymity is so fundamental to our program that our name is based on it. The focus on nicotine and the spiritual commitment to anonymity are essential elements in what distinguishes our program of recovery from other group programs. By honoring Tradition Twelve, members come to realize spiritual benefits that help maintain our fellowship and support the recovery process.

Anonymity levels all of us evenly. This equality fosters a sense of unity, a power greater than lone individuals. Our common welfare depends upon unity and self-sacrifice, as affirmed in Tradition One. By humbly accepting anonymity, members develop spiritual strength. Anonymity and humility are spiritual partners, each enhancing the other.

In our Third Step Prayer, we ask to be relieved of the bondage of self and self-seeking motives. Our addiction had us behaving in self-centered ways. The mental obsession made us believe that having nicotine was more important than anyone else's well being, even our loved ones. Neither our recovery nor our fellowship can survive self-seeking motives.

Anonymity guides us to serve, rather than govern, moving us to do good in this world and show kindness. Avoiding self-promotion, we are less likely to pontificate opinions about outside issues. Our intentions will be more attractive as we carry the message of Nicotine Anonymous. For our groups to be self-supporting, individual members cannot act in self-interest alone.

Placing principles before personalities, we can better accept *anyone* with a desire to stop using nicotine and stay focused on our primary purpose. Newcomers can feel more welcomed where personality is not the standard by which one is measured. Acceptance furthers us along the path to a spiritual awakening.

The principle of confidentiality is more likely to be honored where anonymity is practiced. This enhances the chances that newcomers will *keep showing up* and begin letting go. Nicotine has no less affect on those with notoriety, wealth, intellect, or any other such "social advantage." We all start at Step One. Similarly, anonymity is there to provide even those of fame with the opportunity to start at Step One and have their confidentiality respected by all members. Confidentiality engenders trust. Where there is trust, the courage to change can receive the support of fellow members. Trust can deepen one's faith in the care and guidance of a Higher Power.

Mindful of Tradition Twelve, members attend to the message rather than the messenger. Humans may slip, whereas principles endure. Humility lets us listen for the truth, whereas pride permits us to believe our own excuses and rationalizations.

Knowing humans may slip, we also realize that confidentiality cannot be guaranteed at meetings, what with newcomers present who are still unfamiliar with this Tradition. Every group's format ought to clearly remind members that confidentiality is imperative to our fellowship's survival. Trust is precious and all members need to treat it with care.

However, following the practice of using first names only, does not mean a person cannot use a last name within the confines of a group or at fellowship functions. There may be times that using first and last names facilitates organizational responsibilities or to receive mailings. It is the benefits referred to in this text that make anonymity an essential practice.

Exercising anonymity and humility does not mean we cannot celebrate. Groups may celebrate a member's abstinence or anniversary with applause and tokens. This is not intended to elevate any one member's status, but simply to celebrate the recovery brought about by honest effort and the grace of a Higher Power.

Both our personal recovery and the continued growth of our fellowship require humble anonymity in order to maintain our spiritual path. Self-confidence is healthy when balanced with gratitude for the grace we receive and principles we follow. Our program, being open to a Higher Power defined by each member's own understanding, places principle before personality even at that spiritual level. In a diverse world, the principle of anonymity enables us to come together in a common pursuit and to fulfill our fellowship's primary purpose.

Notes

Notes